THE BRIGADIER IN SEASON

Peter Tinniswood, playwright, screenwriter and satirist, is the author of many highly-praised and award-winning novels, among them *A Touch of Daniel*, *Mog*, *Except You're A Bird* and *I Didn't Know You Cared*. He is currently at work on a new Brandon novel. He has written two other Brigadier books, *The Brigadier Down Under* and *The Brigadier's Brief Lives*.

THE BRIGADIER IN SEASON

Peter Tinniswood

Pan Books
in association with Macmillan London

First published 1984 by Macmillan London Ltd
This edition published 1984 by Pan Books Ltd,
Cavaye Place, London SW10 9PG
in association with Macmillan London Ltd
9 8 7 6 5 4 3 2 1
© Peter Tinniswood 1984
Illustrations by John D. Lawrence
ISBN 0 330 28496 7
Printed and bound in Great Britain by
Cox & Wyman Ltd, Reading

Contents

1   *The Start of the Season*   1

2   *Stumped!*   15

3   *A Day in the Life of*   29

4   *Harold Salisbury*   41

5   *A Glimpse into the Future*   59

6   *The Party*   71

7   *Carry on Goering*   85

8   *The Holy Father*   101

9   *"Looknow" Hobson*   115

10   *Miss Roebuck's Diaries –*
The Journals of a
Cricketing Spinster   135

11   *The Brigadier in Season*   157

For James Hale and Giles Gordon

ONE

The Start of the Season

The swallows have returned to the golf ball museum at Witney Scrotum.

Celandine glows butter-deep in the water meadows at Cowdrey's Bottom.

Skylarks and pipits sing joyously above the massive, towering buttresses of Botham's Gut.

New, shy green growth has appeared on Old Squire Brearley's moleskin typewriter cover.

Everywhere there is the hushed and breathless wonder of impending Alec Bedser and imminent Richie Benaud.

Yes, it is the start of another cricket season, and Mother Nature has girded her chaste young loins in all her finery to welcome that noblest of summer games.

The signs are everywhere around us.

Derek Randall, blinking sleepily in the bright, spring sunshine, has already emerged from his long winter hibernation spent in the darkest depths of his cricket bag buried in the compost heap at the bottom of his bedroom.

Don "Sir Oswald" Mosey, the leader of the BBC Blackshirt Brigade, is drilling his ball-by-ball commentary team in the indoor claret repository at the rear of the Baxter Arms.

Our bird-watching expert, Miss Roebuck from the dog biscuit shop, reports the first sighting of summer migrants in the valley bottom by Dredge's Elbow.

Garner's long-legged stilt, Hadlee's pimpled rock-hopper, the double-jointed Rice bird, Richards' lissome boundary stalker – what a welcome addition they make to our drab and skulking native fauna.

As for myself, spring has returned to course rampantly through my veins.

My plus-fours throb with anticipation, my stumper's mallet is firm and erect, and there is welcome and unaccustomed movement in the nether regions of my popping crease.

Yes, it is without a shadow of doubt the "finest time of the year".

Begone dull winter and the horrors of stale bedsocks and the moving television screen.

Could there possibly be a fate more ghastly for lovers of the "summer game" than being trapped in the sitting room of a Saturday evening with the lady wife and her loathsome unmarried sister from Cheltenham watching "3–2–1"?

What do I care if some vile, scrofulous, slack-jawed, adenoidal, concave-shinned, stoop-shouldered, blue-chinned, monosyllabic, pasty-faced, typically gormless, bronchial Northern couple win Dusty Bin?

I am not a prejudiced man, but in my opinion every single person who appears on the moving television screen during the dog days of winter should be thrashed within an ounce of its wretched life, boiled in oil, tarred and feathered, hung, drawn and quartered and, horror of horror, be compelled to watch endless action replays of Mary Poppins-Parkinson's elocution lessons.

Scum, the whole man jack of them.

Is there no respite from Hugh Scully?

Is there no refuge from "Whispering" Ted Lowe, Reichsmarschall von Pickering and Dame Clive James Superstar?

Is there no reprieve from Nigel Smarmer-Stiff?

Bring back Clay Jones, I say.

Let the nation rise up in protest and demand the return of Jasmine Bligh and W. Barrington Dalby.

I for one am prepared to stand up and be counted in my determination to "do my bit" for the restoration of Sylvia Peters.

But enough of these matters.

Spring is upon us.

Lambs gambol.

Rooks rasp the elms.

In creaky old Farmer Emburey's paddock the

shire horse foal wobbles and weaves on splayed and stilted legs, for all the world like Colonel "Mad" Bob Willis bowling the first ball at the Adelaide Test.

Summer, to use the immortal words of E.R. "Elizabeth Regina" Dexter, is "acumen in" and our moving television screens will soon purr and swoon to the sensuous rhythms and cadences of Jim Laker and Dame Peter, the "summer game's" unparagoned answer to the ghastly Minge and Thwackett.

I sit now in my study at Witney Scrotum surrounded by the souvenirs of my late lamented and much detested father and watch with pleasure the smoke ascend from the Commodore's chimney into the clear spring sky.

What is he burning today?

More shavings from his mother's wooden leg?

Waste material from Mr Dennis Lillee's armpits?

Relics of St Kevin de Keegan's endorsements?

Is there anything more redolent of the timeless virtues and noble traditions of our beloved English countryside than fresh, unfettered chimney smoke?

It is spring and our imaginations run riot as we think of the joys to come.

As that bloody idiot, the poet, said:

"For, lo, the winter is past, the rain is over and gone.

"The flowers appear on the earth; the time of the singing of birds is come; and the voice of the new year's *Wisden's* is heard in our land."

In our minds there is one question and one question alone uppermost – what will the new season bring?

How well I remember the days of my childhood, when my late lamented and much loathed father would drag me by the ears into his study and bark in those familiar whisky-impregnated tones:

"Well! Who's coming this year?"

My legs would quake.

My cheeks would quiver.

My voice would waver.

"The South Africans?" I would say fearfully.

"No, you swine. No, no, no," he would shout and beat me about the shoulders mercilessly with his Gunn and More sjambok.

And then, with his watery eyes popping and his forehead scarlet and perspiring, he would bellow:

"It's the bloody Australians.

"Get out the poison.

"Load the gin traps.

"Rally the yeomanry.

"*Denn wir fahren,*

"*Denn wir fahren gegen Greg-or-ree.*"

Dear father, how we detested him and his hairy nostrils and his bloodshot ears and his watery teeth and his oval tins of De Reszke cigarettes.

How well I remember his funeral, and the unrestrained cheers of the villagers as he was "laid to rest" in the family vault, which now serves in perpetual honour to his name as the parochial bottle bank.

How well, too, I remember years much later, when Hitler and Musso the Wop having been soundly thrashed, despite the unwarranted intervention of the gum-chewing, fetid-navelled Yanks, we awaited breathlessly what historians will for ever refer to as "the resumption".

Consider this.

For six long, weary, arduous years, through blockade and blitz, through doodle bug and Woolton pie, through Robinson Cleaver and Henry Hall, we had suffered the worst fate known to civilized man – we had been starved and deprived of all contact with the first class game.

Empires greater by far than ours have crumbled through lesser vicissitudes.

Only the inherent nobility and fortitude of the English nation could have survived six bleak years deprived of all contact with Laurie Fishlock and D. V. P. Wright, and only dimly aware of the continued existence of Jas Langridge and P. A. Gibb.

My God, how vividly I recall those post-war years of "austerity" and wet batteries and Rudge bicycles and Leslie Sarony and the *Daily Dispatch*, when bemusedly we surveyed the names of the Indian tourists of 1946, which to our untutored eyes looked for all the world like the ingredients on the label of a jar of mango chutney.

And 1948!

The first visit of the Australians!

What anticipation!

What fervour of excitement!

Ring and Toshak, Hammence and Saggers, McCool and Loxton – could they possibly remember to do up their flies when being presented to King George VI at the Lords Test?

And then the New Zealanders of 1949.

What were we to make of them as we perused the "official manuals" of the tour?

T. B. Burtt – "he is manager of a furniture company".

H. B. Cave – "he is a farmer in private life".

J. B. Reid – "occupation, boot operative".

Yes, in those days of the 'Forties we still had our priorities right.

This was a world in which a man could represent his country with pride and still run a well-conducted heel bar in the pavilion at Lords.

Sutcliffe, Cowie, Mooney, Rabone, Cresswell – unsung heroes, but still to me names to tingle the manly juices, to stiffen the stumps of desire and harden the bails of concupiscence.

My God, how I wish I'd married Martin Donnelly.

And so the years of nostalgia roll by.

1950 – the year of the incomparable, the sublime, the sinuous, sensuous Roy Tattersall who kept a whole nation throbbing feverishly during those long, hot summer nights.

The spring of 1951 – who could possibly have forecast in those innocent, tranquil years that D. F. Jakeman would finish fourth in the batting averages?

1961 – only a soothsayer of the highest calibre could have prophesied that in the September Mr J. M. Lawrence would be presented by Her Majesty the Queen with a new set of dentures "for services to Somerset cricket".

The mist-shrouded, lilac-wreathed April of 1964 – could anyone have guessed that later in that year Glamorgan would have . . .

My God, how I wish I'd married Wilfred Wooller.

And now dusk sheds her rosy mantle over Witney Scrotum.

The yaffle mocks the roost-bound gulls.

The barn owl ghosts the abandoned mint imperial hatcheries at Wellard's Creek.

The beady bats slumber secure in the belfry of our ancient and beloved Saxon parish church of St Christopher and Martin de Jenkins.

And what are my own personal hopes for the coming season?

I confess that they are now more modest than of former days.

Old age comes to us all – yea, even unto Jimmy Hill and Louise Botting – and withers the sapling in its sheaf and droops the mast of aspiration.

I own that at long last I have abandoned all hope of being selected to open the batting for my country with the saintly Mr Winston Place.

I know now in my heart of hearts that never ever shall I "stand" at Hinckley with Mr H. D. "Dicky" Bird.

I have reluctantly reconciled myself to the fact that there is not the slightest chance of my being granted the supreme cricketing honour of wheeling Mr Ray Illingworth's bath chair down the pavilion steps at Headingley when he makes his final appearance as Yorkshire's captain in 1996.

No, it is to my home village of Witney Scrotum that my fondest attentions are now turned.

Already the ground has had its first cut.

And what a splendid sight the operation made as we leaned on the wall watching the village elders, Alston, Arlott and Mosey, crawling slowly over the sward on their hands and knees, cropping the grass with their specially-sharpened steel dentures.

We are, however, like many other teams both famous and humble, plagued this season by problems of captaincy.

Who will take over from old Squire Brearley, is the question uppermost in our minds.

Reluctantly the old chap has had to stand down, for the guy ropes and tent pole which have secured him in an upright position at third slip this past twenty years have at last rotted away, and there is simply no money in the kitty to purchase adequate replacements.

We wish him well in his retirement as he works on his latest "magnum opus", an examination of the philosophical and commercial innocence of the uncapped county player entitled, "How To Use a Sproat to catch a Mackerel".

But who the devil will replace him?

It is the "general consensus" of opinion that the village undertaker and Tupperware representative, Virgin, is at eighty-eight surely far too young to bear the burden of such high office.

Our blacksmith and honorary toad circumcizer, Gooch, has, I fear, ruled himself out of contention through his defection two winters ago to the fleshpots of Keating New Town, where with Farmer Emburey and Wayne "Ma" Larkins of the diddycoi site, he disgraced himself for ever in the eyes of authority by taking part in that town's municipal all-white formation limbo dancing team.

And so a compromise will be reached and we shall appoint the village idiot, poor, old, slavering, twitching, wild-eyed Ben Stansgate.

I console myself with the thought that there are precedents galore of people with absolutely no knowledge of cricket captaining their country successfully at Test match level.

Here I think of Mr Tony Lewis and Mr Donald

"Deborah" Carr, both of whom had outstanding records on the "subcontinent", despite suffering most grievously from constant and violent attacks of the dreaded Nawab of Pataudis.

My mood is made all the more sanguine by thoughts of those "backroom boys", without whom cricket as we know it in Witney Scrotum could not possibly exist.

I think of old Granny Swanton and her devoted band of tea ladies, who, despite a series of unfortunate fatalities involving two visiting stumpers, a third-change seamer, the rector's cousin and a defective batch of cucumber sandwiches, performed so nobly for us on the gastronomic front.

I think, too, of our scorer, shy, retiring, blush-bound Miss Roebuck from the dog biscuit shop, who "at this very moment" will be sharpening her coloured indelible pencils, oiling her abacus and inflating her Frindall patent anti-piles scorer's cushion in preparation for the season to come.

As for the lady wife – well, during the winter she has been busy on her fretwork machine knitting a new set of non-shrink, reversible nets, and these she has erected in our garden in a small patch by the clearing where I normally transplant my used pipe cleaners.

My God, she has been out there pounding down the crimson rambler and already she is in fearsome shape.

She has lost the square-on action which so marred the effect of her late outswinger, and, taking the advice of Colonel "Mad" Bob Willis, has improved her run up beyond measure by wearing her arch supports inside out.

Unfortunately her cricketing prowess will once more be "hidden under a bushel", for until there is a change of rule in our local cricket association allowing people with loud voices and hairy legs to play first team matches, her services will not be used.

However, I have already volunteered her services as auxiliary to the groundsman's horse, which is in desperate need of assistance in pulling the heavy roller.

I am not a prejudiced man, but when I look at the lady wife, and when I look at the groundsman's horse, I have only one thing to say:

My God, how I wish I'd married the grounds-man's horse.

TWO

Stumped!

During the course of a long and arduous life spent in the service of King and country I have seen sights which have plunged me to the depths of misery and instilled into my soul feelings of the profoundest horror and revulsion.

I have seen the innocent victims of blood-crazed fuzzy-wuzzies, opium-sodden pirates of the South China seas and power-mad gate-keepers at Lords.

I have seen the pestilence-ridden slums of old Calcutta, the fly-blown brothels of Bangkok and the inside of Mr Derek Randall's cricket bag.

I have seen Miss Mary O'Hara on the moving television screen.

But these, dear readers, are mere trifles compared with the vision of wretchedness and abject despair which so recently presented itself to my tired and rheumy old eyes.

Picture the scene.

It was a spring morning of a sublime enchantment.

The meadows were aswoop with lapwing and

lark, the swift-laced skies were whoopered with swan and stooped with falcon and still there was no sign of Richie Benaud reaching our shores.

Yes, on such a day a man was proud to call himself English.

Mother Nature sang joyously as she listened to the sounds of "the boyhood of the year" – the soft, sensuous sigh of cricket pads new wakened from long winter hibernation, the merry trill of Bedser twin, new-plummaged for summer in maroon nylon sock and grey plastic mac, the rapturous song of jenny wren as she built her delicate, gossamer nest in Mr David Gower's pubic hair.

My companion sighed with deep contentment.

Dear old Bruce Woodcock of *The Times*.

He was replete with pleasure.

At long last he had achieved his life's ambition – he had just been appointed chairman of the Longparish branch of the Barry Manilow fan club.

I, too, was awash with happiness.

The lady wife was "confined to quarters" with an attack of leg spinner's elbow.

Her loathsome Bedlington terriers were "in dock" once more with severe canine dandruff, the result, I suspect, of sniffing the lining of Mr Fred Rumsey's first change cummerbund.

And, joy of joy, I knew of a friendly watering hole no more than one more nautical mile distant at the village of Swanton-without-Melford where "mine

host" kept a noble cellar of vintage Vimto and
fortified cream soda.

What more could a man ask of life? I opined
myself thus to Woodcock.

But of an instant a dark shadow fell over his dear
limpid features, and the bowl of his bent-stem
Crapp and Richardson pipe let out a long and
mournful "sluck".

"No," he said. "No.

"The echo of joy is despair.

"The hound of happiness is misery.

"For every rapture granted us by Life there is a
torment to plague us."

I was compelled to agree with him.

How else to explain the cricket reports of Mr
Tony Lewis or an innings by Mr Trevor Bailey?

But why?

Why should he, the most sanguine of spirits, cast
such a gloom over our exultations?

I was soon to discover the reason.

Taking off his Gucci stumpers' gauntlets, he laid
his soft, snow-white hands upon my arm and led me
over the sward to a straggled gap in the burgeoning
hedgerow.

"Look," he whispered hoarsely. "Look."

I surveyed the prospect.

And I gasped in horror.

There in front of my eyes I saw it.

Once many many years ago I had seen it with

youthful innocent eyes untainted by the moving television screen and its images of Sebastian Coe's teeth and Daley Thompson's armpits.

How it had moved me, that noble pile of mellow Cotswold stone with buttress and cornice, cool cloister and yielding lawn, lowing chapel bell and shimmering grotto.

Now it lay in ruins.

A wreck.

A stricken rack-a-bones of crumbled stones, shattered windows, sagging walls and gaping roof.

"Good God, Bruce," I said. "Is it? Can it be? Surely it can't be . . ."

"Yes," he said. "Yes."

And a tremble came to his full-red lower lip.

He shook his head sadly and blew his nose on the tail of my shirt.

"Yes," he said. "It is indeed the Royal College of Umpires."

I helped him across the stile and so distraught was he that he did not notice the rent that appeared in the seat of his white satin, Judith Hart autographed pedal-pushers.

We approached the building in silence.

In silence, too, we sat upon the weed-strangled camomile lawn.

Lost in our memories we were hardly aware of each other's presence – for all the world like Lord Henry Blofeld and Mr Bill Frindall commentating at an Old Trafford Test.

The Royal College of Umpires!

Once those words had been spoken in the hushed awe of the most baited of severely baited breath.

Once it had been the most revered and sacred of English institutions, to rank in holiness alongside the pavilion at our beloved Bramall Lane, the birthplace of Dame Peter West and the monastery where the youthful Neil Durden-Smith first discovered he had a hyphen.

And now it was a ruin; defiled, vandalized, in no better shape than a village memorial hall after a bring-and-buy sale organized by the Leeds United Supporters' Club.

How typical of the vileness of the times in which we live!

How typical of this age of decimal numbers, that chap with the bald patch and big ears at Buckingham Palace, cordless pyjama pants, foreign tourists with their damnable rucksacks, postcodes, Australia, athlete's foot, lesbian women of both sexes and those blasted triangles of processed cheese it is quite impossible to get out of the silver paper without squashing the loathsome stuff beyond redemption.

I am not a prejudiced man, but . . .

No.

Let us continue with serenity and calm.

I stood up and left my companion deep in reverie

as he studied the diamante buckles of his Adidas formation dancing pumps.

Slowly and sadly I commenced to walk round the grounds of that ancient and noble establishment which had survived the ravages of Henry VIII, Oliver Cromwell and "Capability" F. R. Brown only to fall victim to the neglect and apathy and self-centredness induced by a generation weaned on instant custard, one day cricket and disposable score cards.

How well I remember it in the days of its prime!

Then it was the overriding, overpowering ambition of every red-blooded, patriotic Englishman with typical clear half moons to his fingernails and ramrod-straight shinbones to "put down" his son at the moment of birth for a place at the Royal College of Umpires.

Tearful mothers might have bewailed the fact that their offspring were snatched from the bosom of domestic bliss at the tender age of three, but none could deny the distinction which was thus conferred upon the family.

To have a son admitted to the college was an honour greater by far than that bestowed upon those families whose progeny were inducted into the monasteries of Tibet or Nepal.

What is beyond doubt, however, is the fact that training at the college was rigorous in the extreme.

It took at least forty years before an ordinand was

considered fit enough to "come out into the world" and play his part as a first-class, fully-qualified umpire.

From the moment he was admitted to the establishment at the age of three and had his head ceremonially shaved by the huge, ornate and wickedly-curved Skelding knife, the novice submitted himself to a life of poverty, chastity and unquestioning obedience.

He was clothed in robes of purest white.

Around his waist were draped cable-knit sweaters of every first class cricketing county and Test-playing country, yea, even Zimbabwe.

Thus garbed he spent his entire daylight waking hours standing completely motionless on the college "square", fingering his rosary of six 10p pieces attached to a cat gut string made from the sacred relics of the blessed David Sheppard's personal corsets.

Later, much later, there would be relief from this immobility when the novice was instructed in the canonical intricacies of the signalling of leg bye and short runs, and made to chant those supremely beautiful words, spoken from time immemorial by umpires waving aside spectators moving in front of rain-swamped sightscreens:

"Sit down, you bloody pillocks."

The regime was no less harsh when the novice had completed his outdoor offices.

In the great refectory, with its ecstatic bas reliefs of "Venus Carrying The Infant Tom Spencer", meals were eaten in a silken silence broken only by a senior umpire reading out loud from the works of St Francis de Chester, His Holiness George Pope and the Blessed Dusty, Supreme Patriarch of Rhodes.

As the angelus bell tolled for the end of luncheon and tea breaks the novices would rise silently from the trestle tables and, with heads bowed and light meters clutched firmly between praying hands, make their way along the cloisters, down the pavilion steps and into the sacred Old Trafford simulator, where they would be subjected to hail, rain, snow and a stereophonic rendition of the massed appeals of George Duckworth and "Ranji" Wilson.

With what emotion I wandered round that ancient pile.

Yes, there distinctively and unmistakably were the remains of the High Wicket where the young H. D. "Dicky" Bird had pledged himself to vows of eternal celibacy.

Yes, hidden beneath the gorse and deadly night-shade was the sanctuary where the adolescent David Constant had been fitted with his first panama hat.

And there, under a mound of ancient rabbit tods, was the very spot where in a sudden blinding flash "the truth" was revealed to the immaculate Bill Alley causing him to cry out:

"I know it. I know it. All has been revealed.

"Wilf Wooller is a twat."

And there, most moving of all, standing defiant from a pile of fossilized lava bread, was the gravestone of the college's most famous son, the Welsh umpire, Llewellyn Yapp.

Nowadays his name is but a distant blur on the far and misty horizons of old mens' memories.

But I remember him still pure and clear from the days of my boyhood.

Ah, how vividly I remember him.

He had the typical features of all members of his branch of the Celtic race – shifty eyes, foxy chin, stunted growth and untrustworthy thumbs.

Yes, by God, what a "character" he was.

It was his custom to travel from ground to ground by Rudge autocycle.

At moments of supreme boredom during the match he would bring the machine onto the pitch and repair it where he stood at square leg.

Years later at Lords Yapp was the central figure in another incident which is written large in the annals of our beloved "summer game".

As is well known to all readers of *The Cricketer*, *Exchange and Mart* and the sadly defunct *Brian O'London's Weekly* Yapp was the inventor of the umpire's portable commode.

This was a subtle and cunning device consisting of porcelain pot and mahogany seat mounted on cast iron castors and attached to the waist by a waterproof harness of fortified Kallicharran leather and Rae and Stollmeyer quick-release buckles.

It served Yapp long and discreetly until one Bank Holiday he found himself "officiating" at a match between Middlesex and Sussex at Lords.

He was standing at the bowler's end, lost in the reveries of a long and deeply profound bowel movement, when he was disturbed by a raucous appeal of lbw by "Big Jim" Sims.

Startled by the strident yell Yapp inadvertently released the handbrake of his commode and to his horror found himself propelled rapidly down the slope at the Nursery End and, striking the boundary fence a most fearsome blow, was shot like a ball from a cannon into the spectators drinking at the Tavern bar.

I am assured by those present that the quality of their beer was improved inordinately by this contact with Yapp and the contents of his recalcitrant machine.

I myself well remember another celebrated incident during the Cheltenham festival when Yapp taking advantage of a "handy" moment between the changing of Mr Charlie Barnett's false teeth took out his fretwork machine and . . .

No, dear readers, I cannot distress myself further

by bitter memories of "days gone by".

Let me conclude by saying that I picked my way back through the ruins and the rubble and rejoined my chum, whom I found sitting forlornly in the remains of the chapel of Saint Sydney de Buller idly picking at the strings of his Mary Quant thigh pads.

Silently we repaired in the trusty Lanchester to his home, the Curacy at Longparish, and there in the Fingleton room we discussed the events of the day.

We were in full agreement – the world today, in which we live, is indescribably ghastly.

Cricketers playing in the dead of night in vile multi-coloured pyjamas, bowlers of mature years embracing their colleagues on the taking of a simple catch in the slips, batsmen kissing and cuddling on the scoring of a measly half century, Australian bowlers having public "tiffs" with their captains on the field of play – has the whole of the first class game been taken over by the nancy boy fraternity?

There is only one thing for it.

Bring back the steel and the sinew into the summer game.

Bring back corporal punishment for non-walkers and persistent appealers.

Bring back the death penalty for no balls and short runs.

Let us once more have transportation for life for being a Chappell brother.

In short – bring back the Royal College of Umpires to restore the decency, the honour and high standards of conduct inherent at the core of this most noble of summer games.

As soon as those words were spoken, dear old Bruce jumped out of his hand-knitted, bamboo sofa, tossed his silk-crocheted balaclava high into the air and shouted:

"Hurrah. Hurrah.

"And there is only one person in the whole wide world who can do this.

"Of course," I said. "It's the Ink Monitor at Number Ten."

What a woman!

Lady Falklander!

She smashed the greasy, unshaven, cowardly Argentinians, she routed the vile, garlic-stinking, money-grabbing Frogs in the detestable Common Market, she soundly drubbed the limp-jawed Lefties with the Campari-stained suede chukka boots and their drooping, malodorous French cigarettes and steadfastly stood defiant against the Yankee invasion of the Grenadian coons.

With her at the helm the British Umpire will once more rule the world.

With her leadership the British Umpire will once more become the greatest power on earth for the dispensation of justice, decency and high moral rectitude.

What a woman!

But, oh dear, I do wish she didn't look so like Arthur Jepson.

And if only she were half as wise.

THREE

A Day in the Life of

My overwhelming, unrestrained and totally un-
qualified admiration for newspapers and all those
saintly people who write for them is one of the
greatest and most enduring comforts of my life.

How grateful I am to have been personally
acquainted in person with many of the true "giants"
of English journalism.

The names simply "trip off the tongue" – L.
Marsland Gander, N. F. S. Creek, Archie Ledbrooke,
Henry Rose, Basil V. Easterbrook, Sidney Salt-
marsh, the beloved and immortal Fred Walters,
Renton Laidlaw, Ewbank Callender, Claude Harri-
son, W. J. Hicks, Neville Cardew, R. C. Robertson-
Hare, Brian Chugg, Enid J. Wilson, and, of course,
most illustrious of all, W. W. St G. Neepsend, for
so many years "points and shunting" editor of *The
Amateur Railwayman*.

Given this enthusiasm and unyielding commit-
ment to the cause of The Fourth Estate it is, therefore, dear readers, easy to understand the loathing
and contempt and downright detestation I feel to-

wards the burgeoning and loathsome colour supplements with their independent pull-out extras.

What I demand from a newspaper is "a damn good read".

And this one palpably and criminally does not get from these so-called magazines with their interminable massed ranks of shamelessly commercial advertisements for fitted kitchens, microwave ovens, automatic home computers worked by electricity, Japanese garden tractors, Danish shower attachments for women with big things on the front of their chests, and book clubs offering nothing but road atlases, yoga manuals and the collected works of "Billy" Liddell-Hart.

And as for the moving motor car advertisements – what right have the Wops and the Huns and the Nips and the garlic-reeking Frogs to publicize their cheapjack merchandise in an English journal?

Who in their right mind would want to buy their loathsome junk in the first place?

I look at my trusty Lanchester, and I think what is wrong with integral windscreen wipers, optional wheels and en suite toilet?

I look back to the days of "my prime" and I refuse to believe that nowadays there is no market for Humber and Lea-Francis, for Armstrong Siddeley and Jowett Javelin, for Frazer Nash and S.S. Jaguar.

It is typical of the nancy boys, lounge lizards and bossy women with tight-fisted bottoms who run these magazines that they would rather kow-tow to the odious johnny foreigner than praise and publicize "their own".

And then, to crown it all, they have the profound impertinence to print on the back page each week an article entitled "A Day in thè Life of".

To my untutored and unprejudiced eyes the subjects of this feature consist entirely of clammy-faced interior decorators, hairy-chested lady writers of childrens' stories and consumptive mobile librarians from the more remote valleys of industrial South Wales.

What waste and disgusting self indulgence.

During the whole course of this vile magazine's existence there has been not one single word about A Day in the Life of Gordon Garlick.

There has been no mention of the domestic routine of the saintly Winston Place, the sublime and sophisticated "Foxy" Fowler and the Immaculate Dental-General to British Land Forces, Lancashire, the Hon. Kenneth Cranston.

And why has Mr G. R. "Noddy" Pullar been so shamelessly ignored?

Good God, he stays in bed all day so his article would take up no space at all.

But no, the scum in the fastness of their editorial castles in the sky jam up their pages with vermin, in whom no decent, red-blooded, God-fearing Englishman could possibly take any interest.

Who in his right mind, for example, would wish to know how often David Hicks shaves and shampoos his armpits?

Is the sum of human happiness made any greater by the knowledge that Iris "Stinker" Murdoch writes her books seated on top of a Wimbledon umpire's chair and is currently working on the fifth definitive biography of Sir Geoffrey Boycott entitled *Under The Net*?

Are we the better in soul and spirit for knowing that Dame Peter West was seated on a Tizer-filled water bed when writing his definitive study of an English cricket writer, *The Meaning of Reason*?

I think not, dear readers, I think not.

What this nation needs is blindingly obvious – an article entitled "A Day in the Life of Imran Khan".

At great personal expense and inconvenience I have myself compiled such an offering, compiled from brief snatches of conversation I culled from listening at the doors of his own personal outside toilet at Boodles.

And this is it:

"I wake about an hour before I have to leave for the cricket ground.

"This is about nine in this country and ten in Pakistan.

"I have, of course, my own personal travelling alarm clock wallah, who attends to these matters, in addition to testing my shower cap, Hoovering my prayer mat and exercising my arch supports.

"I was, of course, brought up personally in the highest circles of Pakistani society.

"I was educated at Aitchison College, the best public school in Pakistan, which used to be called "the chief's college", owing to the fact that it was originally instituted for the sons of princes, maharajas and Sir Richard Attenborough.

"I was then sent to Worcester Old Grammar School in England, and it was the toughest nine months of my life, because I'd never lived away from home before.

"I could not believe the ghastliness of the English winter.

"The television appalled and terrified me – remember I was still a young boy who until then had never dreamed of the existence of Lulu or Mary O'Hara.

"And as for the sanitation – quite grisly, my dears.

"I couldn't believe the toilet paper.

"At home in Pakistan we were accustomed to wiping our bottoms on pages torn from the choicest volumes of the Folio Society, and each member of our family had as of right his or her own personal flushing wallah.

"Incidentally, I should say here and now that our antecedents are not of the land-owning Pathan class, as is generally believed by readers of the odious *Sproat's Cricketers' Who's Who*.

"My father comes from a long line of dental mechanics and with my dear mother emigrated from Hungary shortly before Hitler's beastly pogroms.

"Thus it is that I was originally christened Imre Kahn.

"However, we do not talk about this much.

"Suffice it to say that after Worcester I went up to Oxford and loved it there.

"It was a different world altogether.

"A quite fantastic place.

"I had a few minor shocks, such as when I realized there was a goodly smattering of students of Northern working-class stock present, but I soon discovered I could live with their dropped aitches, their rusting bicycle clips and their disgusting table manners. In next to no time I gained my double Blue for pig sticking and bicycle scrabble.

"At no stage did I decide to make cricket my career.

"I just thought I'd do it for a year to pass the time and then marry into the British Royal Family, even though I find their Greek antecedents slightly offensive.

"Of course I don't have to work.

"Perish the thought.

"When I leave cricket, I shan't work for someone else.

"I shall either become the Nawab of Pataudi or,

equally challengingly, take over the Presidency of the United States of America.

"After a day's bowling I drive home for a nap in my own personal bedroom.

"In Pakistan I drive a Toyota like all the other scum, for I feel that people like I – or even people like me – must at times display the democratic touch.

"Sussex cricket club provides a car for me here in England.

"I don't actually know what make it is.

"I suspect it might be a Rolls.

"I take breakfast – usually just eggs, cereals and caviar.

"Unfortunately I always seem to miss the mango season at home.

"They don't have it here in England, you know.

"Like all my fellow countrymen we keep water buffaloes for their milk, of which I am exceedingly fond.

"I tried keeping them in this country, but it was not a success.

"It was just impossible to find accommodation for them at Lords, and only at Old Trafford were grazing facilities anywhere near suitable.

"So now I have my own personal herd of pedigree Guernseys, which follow me all over the county circuit.

"An hour before the match I usually exercise my

polo ponies.

"Personally I find nothing finer for clearing the brain than riding down junior members of the ground staff, and when the brutes sink to the ground, exhausted and terrified, what fun to toss to them morsels of my own personal poppadums freshly baked by my own personal chef.

"I do not, of course, share a dressing room with the professionals.

"Personally it is not the smell from their armpits or the sight of their dandruff-encrusted pubic hairs I find intolerable.

"It is their quite ghastly working-class accents, which have forced me to insist on my own personal dressing room, where during the luncheon and tea adjournments I can dine in peace and comfort free from the sound of the tea-sluckers, the denture grinders and the wind exhalers, who form the vast majority of the caucus of English country cricketers.

"At home I never ever shower after a match, for I find the sight of my fellow countrymens' brown, scabrous and hairless bodies deeply offensive.

"Besides, we don't have very good facilities.

"In Pakistan Badidas and Paco Rabonne pour Homme are virtually unknown, and there is a desperate shortage of loofah wallahs.

"In Lahore, of course, there is always something to do in the evenings.

"For myself I am not all that keen on attending floodlit public executions and the stoning of adulterers, but I confess to a sneaking feeling for outdoor spelling bees.

"Our evenings usually end by watching videos.

"Personally I like to escape into a good television series or a movie – something like *Z Kardars* or *From Zaheer to Eternity*.

"Here in England I personally occasionally take a girl out in the evening after the match, but in the main I prefer the company of my own personal retinue, who follow me from ground to ground during the season.

"My own personal umpire is an agreeable fellow, who at times can be quite amusing with his impersonations of Alec Skelding and Elisabeth Schwarzkopf.

"Generally I retire to my own personal bed at a late hour.

"I always pray before going to sleep – my own small prayers asking the Almighty for health in myself, and instant humility in others with whom I have to deal.

"I also pray for the welfare of my family and the continued improvement of Barclay's accent, which is now proving fairly acceptable to me.

"As for my family – they are exceedingly conservative.

"If I wanted to get married, it would have to be an

arrangement.

"Eligible women are pointed out to you at weddings, Bar Mitzvahs and public beetle drives, although in the end it is entirely up to you.

"I expect I shall probably end up marrying Joanna Lumley, Maria Aitken and Esther Rantzen.

"As for the future – well, I haven't made any specific plans.

"Personally I shall probably end up by forming my own personal private county cricket team, captaining England at hockey and rugger, being appointed Governor General of the BBC and taking over the Jimmy Young radio show.

"Or something equally boring, like being Prince Andrew."

FOUR

Harold Salisbury

The history of our beloved "summer game" has been too often darkened by personal tragedies of the most heart-rending nature.

Here we think of dear, family-besotted Johnny Briggs of Lancashire, who ended his life at the age of 39 in Cheadle Asylum bowling non-existent slow medium left-armers to non-existent Australian openers.

We think, too, of the immortal Colin Blythe of Kent, who was struck down in his prime by the vile, shaven-headed Hun at the Battle of Ypres, aged a mere 38.

We think of the benighted and stricken Albert Trott of Middlesex.

"A hard hitter, an overwhelming fast medium bowler and a safe catcher with huge hands, he liked a pint, was easy going, sometimes mischievous, but the victim in later life of the painful effects of dropsy and later ended it all with a pistol shot in his lodgings at Willesden in August 1914, leaving his wardrobe to his landlady.

"The coroner found £4 in cash."

Tragic?

Yes.

Unbearingly poignant?

Yes.

But nowhere near as tragic or as poignant, I suggest, as the fate of poor Sir Geoffrey Boycott whose ghost was doomed forever to open the innings for Yorkshire into the dimmest mists of eternity in the bleak, black knowledge that never again will he appear with Mary Poppins-Parkinson on a moving television chat show.

I confess, however, that when I ruffle through the "darker side" of the annals of our noblest of noble games, I am most moved by the fateful career of the immortal Harold Salisbury.

No cricketer in the long history of our beloved "summer game" had the consummate power to thrill, to charm and provoke unrestrained joy and laughter in the darkest of hearts.

A smiter of mighty sixes, a bowler of fearsome bouncers, a fielder of dazzling grace and athleticism, a clown of true comic originality and genius, Harold Salisbury was unique.

Crowds flocked to see him play.

He was feted on city streets, worshipped by inky schoolboys and adored by love-lorn housewives.

Handsome, sleek and sinuous, he was indeed "a God among Gods".

Who could have possibly guessed, therefore, that behind that lissome, graceful, boundlessly exultant creature there lurked a hump-backed demon with brooding mien and spite and malice in his heart, a hate-spitting, black-browed fiend, ungenerous, cruel, selfish and ultimately self-destructive?

Who could have guessed the terrible secret Harold Salisbury carried within him deep inside his soul?

He hated cricket.

He hated it passionately.

There now.

The truth is out.

Harold Salisbury loathed, despised and detested every aspect of our "summer game", and, if he had one ambition in life apart from drowning Denis Compton in a vat of Brylcreme or setting fire to E.R. "Elizabeth Regina" Dexter's shirt tail, it was to be a congenital "blocker", a trundler of endless slow medium seamers and a fielder of statuesque clumsiness.

How do I know this?

Well, through the good offices of our daily cleaning lady, Mrs Woolmer, there has come into my possession an almost complete set of the diaries and tape recordings from the talking dictaphone made by Harold Salisbury during the whole course of his career.

Mrs Woolmer, it appears, was a second cousin of

Mrs Dilley, who was in turn sister-in-law of Mrs Parks of Langridge-on-Sea, whose brother married a certain Miss Stovold of Graveney-without-Hignell, who was distantly related to a third cousin of Mrs Humpage, whose uncle was once briefly engaged to a niece of Harold Salisbury's wife's sister.

Thus, inevitably, had the diaries and tape recordings come into the possession of Mrs Woolmer.

Not realizing their intrinsic worth she offered them to the lady wife as her contribution to the jumble sale in aid of The Save Don Oslear For The Nation Fund.

Only "by chance" did I discover them, when I had occasion to visit the cock loft in search of my plus four restorer tablets.

You can imagine the amazement, the horror and the morbid fascination which flooded through me as I read those diaries and played those tapes on the Commodore's electric talking recorder.

Without further comment, therefore, I present to you a few selected items from these priceless memorabilia.

Here, for example, is an extract from a tape Harold Salisbury made shortly before his death:

"When I was a lad, there were only two choices open to us for a career – the abattoir or county cricket.

"The choice to me was obvious.

"The abattoir.

"It was my mother who made me take up cricket.

"What I'd always wanted to be right from a child was a chiropodist.

"I seem to have an affinity for feet.

"What I like particularly is the cheese you get between your toes during long hot sultry summers.

"And I don't think you can beat a good painful ingrowing toenail, do you?

"The nicest pair of feet I've ever seen belonged to Ernie Toshak of New South Wales and Australia.

"When I first saw them I just wanted to sit there and stroke them all day.

"I told him so, and he looked at me long and hard and said:

"'Piss off, you pommie poncehead.'"

And so Harold Salisbury joined his county at the age of 16 and embarked upon a career that was to bring such joy to his fans and such intense misery to himself.

Here he speaks again into the talking dictaphone:

"I remember my début for the county as vividly as though it were yesterday.

"Which, as a matter of fact, it wasn't.

"It was a bloody terrible day.

"The sun was blazing down, there wasn't a cloud in the sky, the birds were singing, the roses were in full bloom – bloody miserable, it was.

"There was one bright spot, though – the opposition just carved through us, and when I went into bat we were 86 for 7.

"Big Reg Perks bowled the first ball to me.

"It was a slowish long hop pitched just outside the leg stump.

"How I longed to pat it back to the bowler.

"But no.

"The demon deep down inside me made me rise up on my back foot and hook it over mid wicket for six.

"The bloody thing went right out of the ground and broke the front two windows of a passing trolley bus.

"The crowd went mad.

"They stood up and they cheered and they waved their caps in the air.

"I was bloody mortified.

"The only bright spot was the verruca I was growing under my left big toe.

"It was a real beaut."

In that match Harold Salisbury, to use the words of the sublime E.R. "Elizabeth Regina" Dexter, burst like a flaming comet onto the firmament of the cricketing world.

He fielded superbly.

He scored 136 in the first innings and he took 11 wickets for 63 runs.

Almost single-handedly he won the match for his county.

Listen now to his comments:

"It was one of the worst moments of my life.

"The skipper came up to me and shook me by the hand and said:

"'Well done, old chap. Well done.'

"Typical of the amateur's arrogance.

"Patronizing sod."

In that first season Harold Salisbury carved his name deeply and indelibly on the walls of cricket's hall of fame.

"It was a bloody awful season for me.

"Absolutely bloody wretched and miserable, it was.

"I got a thousand runs in May and just missed getting 100 wickets for the season when, thank God, I had a catch dropped at third slip off the bat of Joe Hardstaff Junior.

"There were a few bright spots, though.

"The skipper got had up for sodomy.

"Typical bloody amateur.

"Mother at long last sold the autocycle and married the lodger.

"And I had the good fortune to have to miss the last two matches of the season owing to a terrible attack of chinky rot.

"It was a real beaut of a one."

There followed three glorious years of triumph and public acclaim.

On two successive seasons he achieved the double of taking 100 wickets and scoring 1,000 runs.

Sixes flowed from his bat.

Wickets rattled beneath the ferocity of his bowling.

No batsman was safe while he was prowling and stalking his territory at cover point.

And yet?

Here he talks again:

"My God, how I hate cricket.

"It's the food they serve up during the matches.

"Bloody diabolical.

"Limp lettuce and boiled ham day after day after day.

"Our new skipper doesn't eat what we eat.

"He sits in his dressing room and all you can hear is the sound of champagne corks popping and silk knickers thwacking.

"Typical bloody amateur.

"And what about the digs?

"Bloody diabolical.

"You try sleeping four in bed plus the stumper's cricket bag.

"The only consolation is that the cockroaches are usually quite friendly."

And here he talks after scoring a double century against Surrey:

"I was in the dressing room at the end of play, cutting my corns, when the door flew open and in came Jack Hobbs.

"He walked straight up to me.

"He clapped me on the shoulders.

"He shook me by the hand and he said:

"'Well done. That was one of the finest innings it has ever been my privilege to witness.'

"Patronizing old sod."

The last season before the outbreak of the Second World War was indeed "golden and honey-hazed" for Harold Salisbury.

A thousand shimmering runs came in May.

He took ten wickets in an innings against Derbyshire.

He took a hat trick against Lancashire and hit a double century in each innings against Kent.

The selectors, it seemed certain, just could not ignore his claims.

But then the demon struck.

This is how he described the incident on the talking tape many years later as he neared the end of his tragic life.

"Gradually and bit by bit it dawned on me that I was a certainty to play for England.

"Oh bloody hell.

"I brooded about it night after night after night.

"I couldn't sleep.

"Well, who the bloody hell in their right mind would want to play for England?

"There was only one thing to do – play like a dog and get out first ball every time and start bowling slow full tosses and long hops.

"And so that's what I tried.

"Bloody disastrous, it was.

"I got 137 first time and then got 87 not out against Warwickshire in 27 minutes to win the match with one ball to spare.

"At the end of play R. E. S. Wyatt came into the dressing room to congratulate me.

"Patronizing sod."

Despite all his efforts Harold Salisbury was indeed chosen to play for his country in the first test against the West Indies.

Here are his comments:

"I was told about it when the skipper came into the dressing room with a great beam on his face and shook me warmly by the hand.

"Patronizing sod.

"He stank of scent, too.

"I stalked out and slammed the door so hard behind me a pane of glass fell out of the window and damn near severed the stumper's wrist.

"I felt much better after that.

"But not for long.

"I couldn't make people understand – I did not want to play for bloody England.

"As far as I was concerned they could stick their cap and their blazer up their bloody whatsits.

"But no.

"They would not believe it.

"I tried every conceivable way of getting out of it.

"I started making midnight heavy breathing telephone calls to Sir Pelham Warner.

"I wrote poison-pen letters to Wally Hammond and wore ladies' suspenders when going out to bat.

"I told everyone in no uncertain terms what I thought about Learie Constantine and all those nig nogs and coons in his team.

"No use.

"No bloody use at all.

"As the day of the match grew nearer, it was obvious that I'd have to take really drastic action.

"There was only one thing for it – poison Gubby Allen, set fire to the long room at Lords and blow up the House of Commons.

"Why hadn't I thought of it before?

"I prepared myself meticulously.

"I bought a jar of rat poison from Timothy White and Taylor's.

"I bought a box of Swan Vesta matches and a presentation case of Brock's novelty roman candles in varied colours from our local newsagent who, typically for him, hadn't got any change, so I had to wait while he went to change a ten bob note at the greengrocers, and as they hadn't got any change either, he had to go to the Co-op coal merchants, and he got talking there to Lillian Duckworth with the smoker's cough and the big tits, and by the time he'd finished with her and her grizzling and grousing it had come on to rain, so he had to shelter in old man Pollard's front doorway and he thought while he was there he might as well go inside and buy himself a new sports jacket, which he did, though he had to wait to get the sleeves altered on the sewing machine in the attic, and, anyway, to cut a long story short he was on his way back to the shop with my change, when he got into conversation with the Hilton brothers and went to their allotments to pick up some radish seedlings and a bag of horse muck, and by the time he got back to the shop and gave me my change, I'd only five minutes to catch the train to Birmingham, so I didn't even have time to put the 4s 7d in my purse and raced out of the shop and, bugger me, I was knocked down by an LMS parcels van and spent the next seven months in hospital with a broken pelvis.

"It was bloody marvellous.

"Les Ames came in once or twice to see how I was getting on.

"Patronizing sod."

The war years came as a blessed relief for Harold Salisbury.

This is how he described them:

"Hitler did a bloody good job, I thought.

"He bloody near decimated the county ground.

"It was his incendiaries which destroyed the main pavilion and the ladies' tea room.

"Unfortunately they missed the indoor batting school, but they did get number 45, which put the wife out of her misery.

"Patronizing sod."

The great resumption of 1946 with all its promise and all its excitement for lovers of the "summer game" brought nothing but gloom and misery for Harold Salisbury.

However much he tried he could not stop making runs or taking wickets.

The inevitable happened – to his intense dismay he was chosen to play in the Third Test against the Indian tourists.

This was his reaction:

"Bloody curry bashers.

"What do I want with playing against them?

"Patronizing sods with their public school accents and their hairy arseholes."

It was the incident pertaining to his unfortunate selection for England, which was to lead ultimately, I believe, to Harold Salisbury's tragic end.

Arsonists are not generally welcomed in the "summer game".

And thus it was that when Harold Salisbury was caught red-handed setting fire to the Nawab of Pataudi's underpants in the ladies' bicycle sheds at Hove, retribution was swift and decisive.

He was hauled up before the authorities at "Headquarters" and banned instantly and *sine die* from cricket.

Of course, in order to "hush up" the incident and

spare Pataudi from the embarrassment of having it revealed to the world that he bought his undergarments in a job lot from the famous departmental stores, Tich Freeman, Neil Harvey and Bob Willis's, the authorities concocted a tale for public consumption.

This is how Harold Salisbury describes it:

"What a bloody performance.

"Those bloody stuffed-shirts at Lords decided to tell the press that I wasn't playing for England in the next test because I was having to retire, owing to the fact that I was suffering from a rare tropical disease which destroyed the central batting system and killed the natural outswinger stone dead.

"Of course, the bloody idiots swallowed it hook, line and sinker.

"What they know about cricket could be written in capital letters on my right big toe.

"John Arlott came into the dressing room to offer his sympathies.

"Patronizing sod."

Harold Salisbury was, of course, delighted to be free at long last of cricket.

But the incident at the ladies' bicycle sheds at Hove had "left its mark".

Inevitably and tragically the decline set in.

Try as he might, he could not fight the arsonist tendencies which overtook him and eventually consumed him.

Here, near the very end of his life, are the ramblings of his last recordings on the talking tape:

"It was me who set fire to the Reichstag, you know.

"Oh yes.

"It was me.

"I did Garlick and Kings's, the quality tobacconists, too.

"Oh yes.

"I did that.

"And I did the Warner Stand at Lords and the QE2 and the Empire State Building.

"I did them all.

"Oh yes.

"It was me."

The tape continues in a confused, disjointed and mumbling monotone.

It is not surprising that two days later he met his death.

This is how he forecast it:

". . . and I burned down Wembley Stadium and Anfield Road and Bradford Park Avenue and the centre court at Wimbledon and the BBC Television Centre and . . .

"And now I'm going to burn myself.

"Oh yes.

"I've got all the gear.

"Firelighters, kindling wood, paper, Bryant and May safety matches.

"Oh yes.

"I've got all the gear.

"And now I'm going to end it all.

"In the outside lavatory at the bottom of the garden.

"Oh yes.

"That's where I'll do it.

"I'll do it in the outside lavatory.

"I'll do it there, relaxed of mind, content of soul, guiltless, conscious-free and fully-prepared to meet my Maker.

"Patronizing sod."

FIVE

A Glimpse into the Future

It is my firm opinion that dining in company with a member of the opposite gender, whatever her sex may be, is an abomination to be avoided at all costs by lovers of our dear "summer game".

Women have an innate propensity for "dragging things out".

Consider their attitude towards arguments, shopping, ablutions activities, hanky panky on Friday night with the lights out and, of course, food.

I am not a prejudiced man, but I believe that any meal which takes longer than five minutes to consume, digest and ultimately evacuate through the "normal channels" is a complete and total waste of time.

Food is made to be bolted back as rapidly as possible.

My late, lamented father of loathsome and detested memory once kept a cross-bred staghound/Norwich terrier of awesome longevity which never once took more than seven seconds in consuming its evening meal.

It lived to the ripe old age of 27, which in human terms is 189 – or nearly half as old as Ray Illingworth – and not one day's sickness did it have until its ultimate and untimely demise through the agency of a cracked bidet on the second day of the Bath Festival.

If that isn't an example to us all, I do not know what is.

It certainly was to my father who, in memory of his dear departed four-legged chum, thereafter studiously avoided all contact with bathroom furniture and ate most of his meals out of the dog's bowl in an unlagged shed at the bottom of the garden.

With such a background my attitude towards food, dogs, bidets, garden sheds, feeding bowls and the second day of the Bath Festival was indelibly forged.

Imagine my horror, therefore, when the lady wife informed me she intended "throwing" a dinner party.

If there is one thing in the world I loathe more than dinner parties it is children with large pink transparent ears.

If there is one thing I loathe more than jug-eared children it is Wimbledon fortnight with its mass public display of varicose veins, schoolgirl acne and sacerdotal bottom-pinching.

And if there is one thing I loathe more than mixed doubles and mixed ballroom dancing on the moving television it is people who talk at mealtimes.

It is my opinion that food should be consumed in total silence.

Eating is an odious enough business without being subjected to a constant spray of half-digested cauliflower cheese and sodden fragments of toad-in-the-hole while one's fellow diners talk incessantly about the price of undersealing their hideous Japanese motor cars.

And that, dear readers, is the heart of the matter as regards my attitude towards dinner parties.

Thus, when the lady wife informed me of her intentions, I curled my upper lip, released a painful ruck in the seat of my underpants, and staring straight into her piggy little eyes, said:

"I see.

"And are you doing the cooking, or will the food be nice?"

With typical lack of concern for my welfare and well-being she ignored the question and further compounded my misery by stating that her invitees were Miss Roebuck from the dog biscuit shop, Miss Slocombe from the mobile acupuncturists, and Old Squire Brearley's housekeeper, companion and dearest confidante, Frau Leibnitz.

A dinner party with four women!

A dinner party at which I should be the sole male!

A dinner party with Miss Roebuck bursting into tears, blushing to the roots and popping her cultured pearls at every mention of Colin Dredge!

A dinner party with Miss Slocombe constantly secreting bits of gristle down the legs of her thermal knickers and the nauseous Hun woman smoking menthol cheroots and complaining non-stop about her employer's batting grip.

There was only thing to do.

As always in times of emergency and direst distress I jumped forthwith into the driving seat of the trusty Lanchester and made my way "at all possible speed" to the residence of my dearest of dear friends, "Bruce" Woodcock of *The Times*.

And as always that precious and kindly soul greeted me with unrestrained warmth.

I admired his new *crêpe-de-chine* jodhpurs and his mauve silk fisherman's smock, and repaired with him to the familiar, dusty, rumpled, malodorous depths of his study, the celebrated Fingleton Room.

There, "generous to a fault", he plied me with drinks. ·

Home-made Elastoplast brandy and from his recent tour of Australia two superb bottles of Château McGilvray temperance port and a demi-cask of Schloss Wessels Spaetauslese smoky-bacon flavoured hock were washed down with cow udder sandwiches and kipper paste sherberts.

What bliss!

And as the hours "slipped away" and soft barn owls called to the dusk and nightjars churred in ferny thickets he accorded me one of the most intimate favours a man can grant to a "kindred" spirit.

It was, of course, "a peek" into next year's *Wisden's* book reviews.

It is perhaps generally not known that dear old "Bruce" Woodcock, apart from being chief men's fashion editor of *The Times* and Longparish correspondent for *Cage Birds* and *Fur and Feather* is also editor of the cricketers' "bible", *Wisden's Almanack*.

I was stunned by his generosity.

I was overwhelmed by his indiscretion.

Good God, there are unsavoury characters who would pay millions and millions of pounds to gain a sneak preview of an unpublished *Wisden's*.

In unscrupulous hands goodness knows what damage could be done with foreknowledge of the Five Cricketers of the Year.

The mind boggles and quivers at the thought of the disasters that could ensue if agents of a foreign power were to gain access to unpublished proofs of the latest J. B. G. Thomas dissertation on the state of Glamorgan cricket – absolute dynamite.

And yet, dear readers, there I was, leafing through pristine fresh book reviews upon which my chum had not yet had time to apply his lime green Teddy Tail blotting paper.

"Are you quite sure, Bruce? Are you quite

certain?" I said. "Do you mean I can actually read these reviews personally?"

"Of course," said Bruce, lounging expansively on his sofa dressed, after his customary swift sartorial change, in nothing but MCC kaftan and I Zingari boudoir cap. "You can print the blasted things for all I care."

And thus I do, in the fullest knowledge and gratitude for the immense privilege granted to me.

I hope, dear readers, that you, too, appreciate the enormous significance of this gesture.

Here are some of the "choicest" items:

A HISTORY OF BICYCLE CRICKET
By Squadron Leader Biffen

"Squelchy" Biffen's diverting and comprehensive history of bicycle cricket satisfies a long-felt need by recording in intricate detail an unjustly and scandalously neglected aspect of the summer game.

The writer skilfully and sensitively traces the course of the sport from its earliest antecedents as a blood-letting rite practised by Mongol and Kentish horsemen on the Steppes of Asia to its present-day popularity as the national game of Kenya, Uganda and "parts of" Zimbabwe.

He recalls many of the past and present

heroes of the game – W. G. N'Grace, Winston N'Place, Malcolm N'Nash and the immortal H. D. G. N'Leweson-N'Gower and his son, N'David.

It is at once balanced in perspective and admirably condensed considering the complexity of the source material available.

THE WAR OFFICE OFFICIAL BIOGRAPHY OF SIR GEOFFREY BOYCOTT, *Volume Nineteen – Aged 11 to 11½: The Fledgling Flexes His Wings*

And so this definitive work on the life, times and thoughts of one of this country's most distinguished sons continues its noble progress This volume produces a wealth of previously unpublished correspondence between the young genius and the Mahatma Gandhi, Mao Tse Tung, Princess Alice of Athlone, George Formby, John Foster Dulles, Frank Lowson. Jean Paul Sartre, Cecil Beaton, Sir William Walton and O. S. Nock.

It deals in some detail with the visits paid to Boycott's home in Fitzwilliam by statesmen of world stature seeking his advice on some of the thorniest problems of modern times.

It confirms, as has long been suspected, that it was Boycott's influence which brought to an end the Korean War, the civil conflict in Cyprus and the states of emergency in Malaya and Hoyland Common.

It truly confirms Sir Geoffrey's reputation as the greatest living Englishman since Benny Green.

THE ALEC AND ERIC BEDSER GARDENING BOOK

Written in their usual lively and witty style the Bedser twins have produced another "must" for all lovers of the "summer game" with a gardening bent.

It is packed with handy hints, among the most useful being the following written by Alec Bedser:

"In my opinion the best sort of garden is one that does not have grass and flowers and things like that.

"In my opinion a garden should consist entirely of concrete and garden gnomes and things like that.

"In my opinion the best sort of garden gnomes to buy are those modelled on myself and my brother.

"As we are identical you could buy a job lot at half price.

"In my opinion that is not to be sneezed at."

The Raising of the
RAYMOND ILLINGWORTH

In the summer of 1982 the whole nation was entranced by the raising from years of neglect and obscurity of one of Britain's most famous wrecks, the *Raymond Illingworth*.

Given the personal sponsorship of the Prince of Wales who took an intense practical interest in every aspect of the operation, this is one of the most romantic and amazing rescue stories of all time.

For years experts had maintained that the restitution of the *Raymond Illingworth* was an impossibility far beyond the technological resources of modern industry and medicine.

They were proved wrong.

From disaster to triumph, from despair to joy, the story unfolds to its magnificent conclusion when watched by millions of enraptured television viewers the wreck was finally raised.

It can now be seen at Scarborough in all its former glory, its upperworks preserved for all time in linseed oil and Safeways sherry.

Received and acknowledged by the editor:

A History of the Tea Interval
An Illustrated Guide to the World's Great

Sightscreens
Harry Makepeace – a Study in Infamy
Indian Cricket, Volume Six – a Hundred Years of Cricket Between Bombay Nude Onanists and the Bengal State Dry Cleaners
Wisden's Anthology of Benny Green

Finally my own personal favourite:

A CRICKETERS' SONG BOOK *Edited by Leslie "Percy" Holmes and Leslie Sohoni*

This indeed is a must for all cricketers of every age and every background.

For rain-stopped-play intervals.

For West Country tours at Easter.

For long, tedious flights to Australia.

For jolly evenings of conviviality and merriment in the bar of the pavilion on Saturday nights.

For all of these and stacks and stacks more this volume provides a compendious selection of some of the most popular songs known to the "summer game".

Here is a brief selection of the most well-loved:

"I'm Just A Girl Who Can't Say Snow"
"Miandad's A Dustman"
"Sit Down You're Rocking The Foat"

"Return To Fender"
"Hullo Young Govers"
"Bedser, That's My Baby"
"Nayudu Something To Me"
"I'm Pilling, Reidy and Abel"
"Pleass, Pleass Don't Eat The Dhosis"
"Dilley of Laguna"
"What Do You Want To Make Those Dyes
    At Me For?"
"Take Me Back To The Slack Hills"
"Hever Jolly Good Fellow"
"I'm Garner Sit Right Down and Write
    Doug Wright A Letter"
"Emburey Little Breeze Seems To Whisper
    Louise"
"Days of Kline and Bosies"
"Tip Toe Through The Duleeps".

We understand that these songs are shortly to be released on a long-playing gramophone record sung to the music of Geoff "Glenn" Miller and Wes "Henry" Hall by Charlie "Anita" Harris and Sylvester "Petula" Clarke.

What an honour to have seen these reviews. Who knows, next year dear old "Bruce" might give me a sneak preview of the following summer's batting averages?

SIX

The Party

Like all lovers of our dear "summer game" I have but one word to describe the politicians who despoil, besmirch and foul the name of this noble and upright old country of ours.

That word is scum.

Scum, trash, dregs of the earth, rabble, vermin, nauseous riff-raff – every man jack of them.

And every woman jack of them, too.

If there is one thing I detest more than sago pudding and show jumping from Hickstead it is lady MPs of both sexes with their false moustaches, hairy ankles and crinkled toenails.

I am not a prejudiced man, but if I had my way, I should consign them instantly to that graveyard of contemporary history – Iain Sproat's *Cricketers' Who's Who*.

Thus it was that earlier in the year I greeted with unrestrained glee, joy, relief and boundless hope for the future the formation of the new political party, the CP – the Cricketers' Party.

For far too long we people of a cricketing "bent"

have been totally and scandalously ignored by the professional politicians in the so-called Palace of Westminster.

The Ink Monitor at Number Ten and her greasy-quiffed cronies with their boil-pocked necks spout endlessly about the unemployed, the underprivileged, one-parent families, the Dagos, the coons, the miners, the dockers, the car workers and similar quite unspeakably disgusting scum.

But what about us?

What about the cricketers of this country?

Have they ever spared a single thought for us?

Good God, without us this dear land of ours would be on its knees, a quivering, shaking, stricken wreck skulking in the wings while the Russians, the Yanks, the Frogs and similar vermin strutted and postured in the spotlights of power.

Tell me this:

Who won the Battle of Britain?

Cricketers, of course.

Who knocked the living daylights out of Musso the Wop in the desert?

Cricketers.

Who won the Ashes from the Australians in 1953?

Well, it certainly wasn't Iain Sproat or Lulu and her chubby little legs.

It was profound and deeply important thoughts such as those which sparked off the first glimmerings of the idea for the formation of the CP.

When Roy "Roly" Jenkins and David Steele of Northants formed their SDP party a couple of years ago, I confess that we cricketers had our hopes that they would concern themselves with our interests.

Not a bit of it.

I personally wrote a written letter to David Steele asking him to spell out in detail his party's policies regarding the burning issues of the day – changes in the no ball law, the state of three day county cricket and the length of Mr H. D. "Dicky" Bird's toenails.

Not a single solitary word did I receive in reply.

Typical.

Well, all that will be changed.

The CP was formed, dear readers, to protect *your* interests.

If you yearn for the glorious days of England's towering greatness, when the tram car and the horse trough ruled our city streets supreme, when children were given decent Christian names like Alfred and Wilfred and George not Wayne or Darren or Kirk, when a man could have a bath in peace and comfort without being constantly badgered and bullied by the lady wife to take his pipe out of the soap bowl, then there is only one answer – VOTE CP.

But, no, enough of this.

Let the policies of our party "speak for themselves".

Let us move back in time to the autumn of 1983

and the first annual conference of the Cricketers' Party.

It was held, of course, at the Royal Dexter Imperial Hotel, Langridge-on-Sea.

In those elegant and gracious surroundings delegates from all parts of the country, yes, even from Yorkshire, mingled and gossiped, wined and dined and, of course, concentrated their attentions on the major issues of moment.

Through the medium of the Commodore's portable talking tape recorder machine I am able to bring you extracts from some of the most important speeches and "policy statements".

Let us commence with the contribution of the Shadow Minister for the Arts, Mr Barry Wood, who set the audience "alight" with his stirring clarion call:

"What this country's culture needs is clear and blindingly obvious – more bints with gynormous knockers."

Let us plunge into the main body of the rapturously received speech delivered by the party's Shadow Chancellor of the Exchequer, Sir Geoffrey Boycott:

"What I should do – i.e., what my intentions are when we come to power – is this as per follows:

"I should at a stroke remove forthwith and at once all VAT payments on slip catching cradles."

(Tumultuous applause)

"What I should do next – i.e., subsequently – is as

per follows:

"I should make it government policy as a matter of urgency to supply free – and, in addition, at no charge whatsoever – contact lenses for all opening batsmen who wear sweat bands and write their own autobiographies about themselves without assistance or help from anyone else."

(Cheers)

"After this – i.e., the next thing I'd do is as per follows – I should index-link the price of hair transplants to twice the rate of inflation plus the number of spokes on Ray Illingworth's bath chair minus the square root of the total sum of Michael Parkinson's wrinkles.

"And then I shall nationalize Peter May.

"I thank you."

For many minutes thereafter the conference room was in an uproar of hoarse cheers, stamping of cricket boots and waving of printed score cards.

"Order, order," shouted the Speaker Designate, the ubiquitous Mr Barry Wood. "Shut up, you barmy pillocks."

When order was at length restored, up stood the Shadow Minister for Community Affairs, Don "Sir Oswald" Mosey.

In a thoughtful, and at times moving, speech he made the following impassioned plea:

"My friends, we cricketers are noted and always have been for the compassion and concern we have shown for those less privileged than ourselves — supporters of lacrosse, statisticians of ice hockey and trainers of whippets.

"But more even than these unfortunates we show our concern for the most oppressed, the most underprivileged, the most exploited groups of workers in this present-day country.

"I refer, of course, to those Pakistani, Indian and West Indian immigrants who eke out a precarious living playing first class county cricket."

(Applause and "hear hear")

"These simple and naive folk were brought to this country by unscrupulous profiteers with the promise of unlimited supplies of Tizer, sharks' teeth and long-legged blonde ladies with gigantic chests.

"Once here, they have been forced against their will to labour in the most appalling degraded and disgusting institution known to civilized man — the English county cricket season.

"Surely no decent and humane society can tolerate the squalid conditions under which they are compelled to work?

"If this country can spend money on intercontinental missiles, nuclear submarines, subsidies for the arts and magazines for nancy boys and collar and tie jobs, then there is absolutely no doubt in my mind that we can spend money on a policy which will in an instant dramatically and overwhelmingly improve the lot of these poor wretched creatures.

"I refer, of course, to instant and compulsory repatriation."

Every single member of the packed audience applauded this speech to the echo, none more so than the Shadow Chancellor of the Duchy of Lancaster, Mr Clive Lloyd.

Further speeches were made by the Shadow Minister for Sightscreens and Heavy Rollers, Archbishop Fred Rumsey, the Shadow Secretary of State for the Luncheon Adjournment, Miss Roebuck from the dog biscuit shop and the Shadow Foreign Secretary, Sir Geoffrey Boycott.

I am bound to say that his speech made a deep and lasting impression on all those who heard it, and indeed on many of those who did not.

It started thus:

"For a man of my boundless and unlimited talents being Chancellor of the Exchequer is a piece of piss.

"Therefore, in order to exercise my varied and multifarious abilities – and there are a lot of them – I should also become Foreign Secretary with special responsibility for dealing with foreigners.

"Contrary to popular belief – i.e. what most people think – I quite like some folk who weren't born in Fitzwilliam.

"I think Peggy Lee is the tops.

"I like Elton John, too, because he always wears a cap like I do, and he's got a good voice, if you disregard his singing.

"In fact, I like most singers.

"My own personal soubriquet for Charles Azna-
vour is 'shit hot', which I would also apply to
Placido Domingo and that other Spanish git with
the teeth, who sings 'Jaws'."

(Applause)

"And thus when I become Foreign Secretary,
besides taking over Two Way Family Favourites on
the Ed Stewart Show I shall immediately – i.e. at once
– press for the conclusion of an international
non-proliferation treaty.

"In my opinion – i.e., what I think – there is far
too much proliferation in the world these days.

"Too many countries are getting into their hands
a weapon which they cannot control.

"In the old days – i.e., once upon a time – only the
major countries were entrusted with the responsibility of managing the most potent and potentially
devastating force known to mankind.

"Yes, my friends, I refer to cricket.

"There is far too much being played in the world
these days.

"It is being introduced recklessly into countries
which just do not have the background, the
resources or the traditions to cope with it.

"Take a quick look – i.e. a swift shuftie – at the
ICC Trophy of 1982 – i.e. two years ago – and you
will see that in that competition there was the

United States, Gibraltar, Papua New Guinea, Kenya, Canada, West Africa, East Africa, Bermuda, Holland and some place I've never heard of called Bangladesh.

"This has got to stop.

"The Great Powers must show their responsibility and move in.

"Australia, New Zealand, the West Indies, India, Pakistan and ourselves should deny cricket at once and immediately to these minor powers.

"The future of civilisation as we know it is at stake.

"My friends, take an example from us in Yorkshire, where for the past thirty odd years we have successfully and triumphantly stopped the spread of first class cricket to Lancashire."

(Rapturous applause)

And so as the evening drew to its close and the gulls creaked and the gannets plunged and the fulmars glided stiffly in the salty dusk the "great moment" arrived.

Yes, it was the arrival of our leader, our future Prime Minister, our saviour from the miseries of inflation, unemployment and "Match of the Day".

Of course it was the man himself, Colonel "Mad" Bob Willis.

Without comment I offer his speech to you.

"Rejoice, my friends.

"Rejoice.

"This old country of ours is still rampant and supreme.

"Remember the stirring events of the summer of '82?

"Remember the campaign which brought back this nation's self-respect, its pride and sense of identity in those dark days when the faint hearts and doubters tried to sap our will as we fought the enemy from across the seas?

"Yes, my friends, we won a memorable victory over the foe.

"But, by God, it was a close-run thing.

"Only by the narrowest of margins, by skill and by courage, by the awareness of the rightness of our cause and by the divine blessing of Him above did we triumph.

"Rejoice, rejoice – we beat the Pakistanis.

"But I say again – how close it was.

"If Sarfraz had been fit to play in all the Tests . . .

"If David Constant had not been wearing his grannie's contact lenses on that fateful last match . . .

"If, if, if, if.

"Never again will it happen.

"We shall be prepared.

"We shall fight for the oppressed.

"We shall fight for the subjugated.

"We shall fight for those loyal fellow countrymen

of ours who live under the vile yoke of foreign oppression.

"Accordingly I am happy to announce that our first act on achieving office will be to launch a Task Force with the object of liberating Tasmania."

(Wild cheers, gnashing of dentures and singing of patriotic songs)

"Do we have the men?

"Yes.

"Do we have the supplies?

"Yes, yes, yes.

"We shall take out of mothballs this nation's two finest capital ships, HMS *Boycott* and HMS *Gooch* whose rejection from the front line was one of the most disgraceful acts of the previous administration.

"Out of mothballs, too, we shall take the Fleet Replenishment vessels, *Taylor* and *Hendrick*, the frigate, HMS *Larkins* and the ocean-going tugs, *Knott* and *Humpage*.

"Victory will be ours.

"And once more the red and yellow standard of the MCC will fly proud and triumphant.

"Our watchword will be: Make Leon Brittan Great Again."

At this point the talking tape recording machine broke down, waterlogged, I suspect, by the Commodore's unrestrained and cascading tears of patriotism and fervour.

But, dear readers, you have "had enough".

Surely now you are convinced – i.e., have made up your minds – that the future of this country depends upon our standing up to be counted and will cast your votes decisively for the Cricketers' Party.

VOTE CP – BEWARE OF IMITATIONS.

SEVEN

Carry on Goering

For some months during the past summer the Commodore and I found ourselves harbouring vague suspicions that all was "not as it seemed" with his gardener.

It is difficult to say what first provoked our doubts about his integrity and his true identity.

The crunch of his jackboots, the aggressive jut of his jaw and the pink scar weals on his shaven skull suggested to me that he could well be a member of the Yorkshire county cricket committee.

But then again the singularity of his speaking accent, with its guttural glottal stops, its bark and snarl, its mispronunciation of some the most basic words in the English vocabulary gave strong indication that he was none other than Mr Trevor Bailey in disguise.

Matters came to a head one early lilac-lilting summer morn as the Commodore and I sat in the cool, sweet-smelling inner sanctum of his summer house, ruffling contentedly through his collection of cigarette cards.

With movements which in others would have

been described as sensuous and erotic, the Commodore was running his fingers down an Ardath card of the immortal J. C. "Farmer" White.

He was in a reverie of the profoundest bliss, as indeed was I, lost in a Balkan Sobranie-scented radiance of rampant ecstasy, as I lingered through what he claimed was a complete set of Wills Railway Engines of 1936, although I firmly believed (as I still do) that he was missing the express locomotive "Mohamed Ali El Kebir" of the Egyptian State Railways.

However, such was the strength and depth of our friendship that even after a dispute of this vital and overriding importance we were prepared to shake hands and "live and let live".

Yes, dear readers, we were at peace with the world.

Bees droned.

Swallows twittered.

Yaffle and dunnock sang their songs of joy to the summer.

And then?

Then there was the most horrendous and bone-crushing explosion from the direction of the potting shed.

We rushed outside, the Commodore and I, and there, "before our very eyes", we saw the gardener surveying the wreckage of the potting shed, stamping his feet with rage and beating the village idiot, old Ben Stansgate, mercilessly about the head and shoulders with the handle of his rhino skin sjambok.

The Commodore shook his head sadly.

"Oh dear," he said. "Ben's been smoking his pipe again in the cockpit of the Heinkel."

I raised my eyebrows.

What on earth could he mean?

What was the significance of that remark?

A Heinkel?

Good God, was the gardener an Airfix addict?

Had he been sniffing "transfers" or giving himself "a fix" on an illicit fretwork machine?

I was soon to find out.

With great dignity of expression and great calmness of manner the Commodore summoned the gardener to the summer house and confronted him thus:

"Drinkwater," he sàid. "I have reason to believe that you are not the person you say you are."

Not a flicker of emotion came to the gardener's eye.

He stared straight ahead of him.

The Commodore continued.

"I don't quite know how to put this, Drinkwater," he said. "Far be it from me to throw a spanner in the works, but it is my firm opinion that you are one of two people."

Not a ripple of unease crossed the gardener's face.

"Drinkwater," said the commodore. "You are either Hermann Goering or Robin Marlar.

"Which is it?

"Which is it, old chap?

"Tell us."

The gardener suddenly threw back his shoulders, thrust out his chest, clicked his heels and held out his right arm stiffly in front of him.

"My God, it's Robin Marlar," said the Commodore with a deep and despair-racked groan.

"No," said the gardener with an icy smile. "No. I am, sir, Reichsmarschall Hermann Goering. Heil Hitler."

The Commodore surveyed him silently for a moment.

"Well," he said at length. "I suppose we must be thankful for small mercies. At least you're not a bloody Australian."

The gardener smiled his icy smile again.

"Will there be anything else, *mein Herr*?" he said.

The Commodore scratched his chin.

"Yes," he said. "Would you be most awfully decent and carry on watering the pelargoniums?"

"*Jawohl*," snapped the gardener and, turning on his heels smartly, goose-stepped out of the summer house.

We looked at each other in silence.

The yaffle cackled.

"Cuckoo, cuckoo," came the call from the distant water meadows at Cowdrey's Bottom.

I decided to take the bull "by the horns".

Decisive action had to be taken.

There was one thing to be said immediately, which was of paramount and vital importance.

I said it.

"For God's sake, don't tell the lady wife."

The Commodore blanched "visibly".

"Good God, no," he said. "She'd be bound to snap him up for a lecture for the blasted WI."

The distress of my old chum was pitiful to behold as he contemplated the difficulties of his circumstances.

What was he to do?

He was actually employing a convicted Nazi war criminal.

Not even Derbyshire county cricket club had stooped so low in their search for a new captain.

Should he report the matter to the authorities?

Conscience and social duty demanded that he should.

But, if he did, where the devil would he find a new gardener?

Everyone knew that they were rarer by far in contemporary England than renegade generals from the former Third Reich.

Gently and tenderly I laid him to rest in his favourite snuff-encrusted armchair and persuaded him to "fill me in" on the full circumstances of the history of the engagement of his gardener.

This he did with unrestrained signs of relief.

Apparently he had answered an advert in *The Cricketer* which had gone thus:

Portly gentleman of Central European extraction seeks post as gardener/groundsman/odd
job man.

Impeccable credentials. Good with children. Played cricket at representative level.

It sounded "too good to be true".

The Commodore sent for him, interviewed him,
"liked the cut of his jib", and forthwith engaged
him.

At first his work and his demeanour had proved
totally satisfactory.

But then the Commodore began to have his
suspicions.

"It was difficult to put my finger on any one
specific thing," he said to me.

"I mean, I thought it a bit odd when he started
calling me '*mein Herr*' and leaping to his feet and
clicking his heels every time I entered his shed.

"I mean, old boy, even Brian Sellars stopped short
of demanding that from his Yorkshire professionals."

The Commodore kept his doubts to himself, but
then the gardener turned his attentions to the
long-disused tennis court at the bottom of the plum
orchard.

"I don't know why he did it," said the Commodore. "One minute it was a lovely old tangle of
weeds and rambler roses and blackbirds' nests.

"Next minute he'd flattened the whole lot,

gravelled it and surrounded it with high barbed wire fences, towers, floodlights, air-raid sirens and men patrolling with long-haired Alsatians.

"I called him in and I said:

"'Drinkwater, are we expecting John McEnroe for the weekend?'"

The Commodore scratched his pate with the stem of his Crapp and Richardson bulldog pipe.

"I never knew what happened to it, you know.

"I think old Ben Stansgate burned it down with his thin Bristol shag."

A couple of years later came another shock for the Commodore.

"I woke one morning," he said, "and there, standing in the centre of the lawn, was what looked to me remarkably like a Junkers JU 88 bomber.

"I called the gardener into the study immediately and challenged him on the matter."

"What did he say?" I asked.

The Commodore shrugged his shoulders.

"He told me it was a new device for propagating chrysanths."

"And was it?" I said.

Once more the Commodore shrugged his shoulders.

"I don't know," he said. "Old Ben Stansgate burned it down with his herbal tobacco."

By now the day was drawing to its close.

"You and Yours" had long since come and gone on the talking wireless.

Dusk was cascading sinuously through the old elms at the rear of the Graveneys' temperance hamster farm.

"So what are we going to do now?" I said.

The Commodore rose from his armchair and patted me on the shoulders.

"We'll do what every patriotic, red-blooded, decisive-minded Englishman would do under the circumstances," he said.

"Which is what?" I said.

"Sleep on it," he replied.

This I did.

But I confess that after concluding my nocturnal ablution activities and repairing to the conjugal container, sleep did not come easily.

Beside me lay the supine form of the lady wife, and as I squinted at her through half-closed eyes, I swear her body took on the shape and size of a Dornier Do 215 night fighter with six gun solid nose.

My God, the enormity of the secret I held.

The responsibility of it all.

In the past I had successfully held secrets of similar import.

For years I had not breathed a word to E. W. "Gloria" Swanton that it was Michael Melford who had sat on and totally destroyed his collection of the entire records of Freddie and the Dreamers.

Never once had I intimated by deed or word that I knew the identity of the English Test all-rounder who had been discovered in *flagrante delicto* with a South African "utility" wicket-keeper dressed in nothing but a black velvet singlet and rubber bowler hat.

My lips had been sealed for ever over the truth surrounding the controversy over the disappearance of Sir Leonard Hutton's clockwork fountain pen in the ladies' press box at Bradford Park Avenue.

But this secret?

How could I contain that?

I had a duty to my King and country.

What to do?

Should I creep out of bed and ring up my old friend Chapman Snitcher of the *Daily Express* and "blow the gaff"?

No.

That would never do.

The Commodore's reputation would be irretrievably ruined in the golf club.

Should I "under cover of darkness" sneak out into the night and set light to Goering as he slept peacefully and unsuspectingly in his quarters in the garden shed?

No.

I could not risk destroying the Commodore's slug pellets in such a wanton manner.

Next morning I made my way, troubled and riddled with tiredness, to the Commodore's summer house.

He met me with a dark and gloomy frown.

"I didn't sleep last night," he said.

"Neither did I," I said.

"Ah," said the Commodore. "Wearing the lady wife's nightie again, were you?"

We looked at each other in despair.

What the devil were we to do?

It was not long before we were provided with the answer.

Just as we were about to take the first snorters of the day (shortly before nine a.m.) the door of the summer house opened and in came Goering, dragging behind him a large tin trunk.

He spoke at once in soft, compliant and pleading tones.

"I know I have done you great wrong," he said. "I throw myself on your mercy and your compassion.

"Please, please, I beg you, let me retain my job and in return I shall present you with this trunk and all its priceless contents."

Silence.

The Commodore and I looked at each other.

Then the Commodore spoke.

"Drinkwater, we'll . . ."

"Goering," said the gardener. "The name's Goering."

The Commodore nodded.

"All right then – Goering," he said. "We'll take a shuftie inside and see what you've got."

The gardener stepped forward, clicked his heels, bowed his head from the neck and opened the lid of the trunk.

The Commodore peered inside and of an instant stepped back with a gasp of amazement and astonishment that caused the edible dormice in the rafters to scuttle for cover.

"Good God," he said. "Good God."

He beckoned me to his side.

"Look inside," he said. "Just look."

I did, and my blood ran cold and the hairs stood up on the back of my neck.

There in the trunk were some of the most priceless and sought-after treasures of Nazi Germany.

We took them out with caution and tingling anticipation.

What were these sixty or so black, leather-bound slim volumes?

Dear Lord above.

They were the personal diaries of Professor Hugh Trevor-Roper – and all personally authenticated by Hitler himself.

And there was the arm band of the Surrey County Cricket Club worn by Doctor Goebbels at the Nuremberg rallies.

And there was Himmler's first *Wisden's*.

And here in the handwriting of the Führer himself was the document proving conclusively, what had long been suspected, that Hess had been flown to Scotland in an abortive attempt to arrange six unofficial five day Tests between MCC and the

Third Reich.

There were other documents and objects which can only be described as "too hot to handle".

If these had been made public, there is not the slightest doubt in my mind that governments would have fallen, monarchies crumbled and even Sir Peter "Wes" Hall's tenure at the National Theatre would have been severely threatened.

There was only one thing to do.

"Bury the whole bloody lot," said the Commodore.

This was done immediately.

Goering worked swiftly and silently as he dug the hole which was to contain the trunk and its dark, black secrets.

Old Ben Stansgate, gibbering softly to himself, lowered the tin container into the pit and in "next to no time" the deed was over and done with.

The Commodore stared long and hard at the gardener.

"There's only one thing that puzzles me, Drinkwater," he said.

"Goering," said the gardener. "Goering."

"All right, all right – Goering," snapped the Commodore. "There is only one thing that puzzles me about this whole business. How the devil did you escape from jail before your suicide?"

Goering smiled to himself.

"It was all so simple," he said.

"The night before I was to die the commandant

came into my cell and said that according to custom I was to be granted one last wish. I had absolutely no doubts as to what it would be."

He paused.

"Well come on, man," said the Commodore. "Spit it out. What was your last wish?"

"To bowl two overs to Joe Hardstaff Junior in the nets at Trent Bridge," said the gardener.

Much to his surprise his wish was granted and that night under conditions of extreme secrecy he was flown to Trent Bridge in an American marine Dakota and there took a net with that noble and sublimely handsome son of Nottinghamshire.

"But what happened?" said the Commodore. "Don't keep us in suspense – what happened?"

"I bowled him middle stump three times," said the gardener.

I thought the Commodore was about to explode. Literally.

His face turned puce.

The veins stood out on his temples and the back of his neck hissed.

"I don't mean that," he bellowed. "I mean, how did you escape and who committed suicide in your place?"

The gardener smiled and then patiently explained in full the circumstances of his escape in a voice that was at once firm but gentle in intent.

We listened entranced.

What a tale he had to tell!

Good God, so that was why Arthur Jepson had had such trouble with his run up?

That was why W. W. Keeton wore moleskin suspenders?

And, dear Heavens above, what a sacrifice made by "Charlie" Harris of blessed and immortal memory.

Chastened and not a little subdued we licked our lips and fiddled with the bottom buttons of our respective cardigans after the gardener had finished his story.

The Commodore smiled.

And then he spoke with a voice quivering with emotion.

"Drinkwater, you may . . ."

The gardener suddenly leapt to his feet and jumped up and down, beating his head with rage.

"Goering," he shouted. "Mein Gott – Goering, Goering, Goering, *du Englischer Schweinhund*."

"All right, all right – Goering," said the Commodore. "All I want to say is this – you may stay in my employ.

"And you may rest assured that your secret is safe with us.

"Right, then. That's that. Carry on, Goering."

The gardener bowed stiffly from the neck again, clicked his heels and backed out of our presence, touching the last vestiges of a damp and compliant forelock.

When he had disappeared from view, the Commodore looked at me and said:

"That's that, then."

"Yes," I said.

"There is only one thing I find difficult to forgive," he added.

"And what is that?" I asked.

"That advert in *The Cricketer*.

"Do you know, I've searched *Wisden's* from cover to cover and I'm damned if he ever played cricket at representative level."

I smiled.

I nodded my head.

"Don't wory," I said. "That's typical of the perfidy of the Huns. Next time I meet Drinkwater, I shall . . ."

"Goering," screamed the Commodore. "Goering, Goering, Goering."

EIGHT

The Holy Father

The summer of '83 was a memorable season of celebrations for all of us in Witney Scrotum.

It started with massed bands, gun salutes and beacons burning brightly on the massive buttresses of Botham's Gut as we celebrated the bicentennial of the discovery of Neil Durden-Smith.

Later in the month the village was decked from end to end in wildly fluttering bunting, fireworks lit up the sky and whole oxen were roasted in the water meadows at Cowdrey's Bottom as we rejoiced in the anniversary of Sir Richard Attenborough's knighthood for services to the world's tiny folk.

Dear dinky little Dicky – to some of the more elderly and simple-minded folk of the village he is the object of considerable cult worship, and rumour has it that old Grannie Swanton has several relics of the great man's quiff hidden in a pair of old thermal coms underneath her bed.

On midsummer's night the whole village gathered *en masse* round the gaunt old henge standing remote, cold and ghostly on the highest point of the lonely Rumsey Downs, reminding us that thousands and thousands of years ago in the mists of antiquity there was an ancient culture who walked with a shuffling, stoop-shouldered gait, communicated with each other in high-pitched grunts and hoarse squeaks, buried their dead in cricket bags and are thus considered to be the direct ancestors of Mr H. D. "Dicky" Bird.

We stood silently with heads bowed as the chill mists rolled up from the valley bottom and soft plovers shivered and we gave thanks, each in our own individual manner, for that holiest of holy, chaste and celibate of Druids, William Frindall, and His Honourable Order of Vestal Virgin Cricket Statisticians.

No sooner was this festivity concluded than there came a succession of "bean feasts", as we made merry with displays of free-fall wicket-keepers and musical nets, given by the Suicide Squad from the Lords groundstaff, to commemorate the birthdays of H. D. G. Leveson-Gower, O. S. Nock, the saintly Winston Place, Dame Googly Withers, the much-loved Arsenal footballer Don, and his historian brother, Trevor, and Brad Ashton and his beloved mother, Sir Frederick Ashton.

I am sure there was something else we celebrated, too.

What the devil was it?

Ah, yes.

I remember.

It all comes back to me now. It was the visit of the

Pope to Witney Scrotum.

I confess that when it was first mooted I had "my doubts".

Would it bring on another of Prodger the Poacher's strange "turns" and set him off once more exposing himself in the mobile library?

Would the sight of all those handsome, single, unmarried, bachelor priests be "too much" for Miss Roebuck of the dog biscuit shop?

What would be the reaction of that raving, ranting, vitriol-tongued preacher, old Doctor Jones-Jones-Ontong-Wooller in his tin hut chapel of the Church of the Third Wicket Down Redemption?

One thing, of course, was absolutely and totally certain – the Commodore was incensed.

"What do we want with a gang of Wops in the village?" he thundered.

I explained as patiently as I could that the Holy Father was of Polish extraction.

The Commodore glared at me silently for a moment, grinding at the stem of his self-lighting bulldog pipe.

And then he said:

"That is as maybe. But I will wager you one silver half crown that the blighter's almost certain to be a bloody Catholic."

Much later we were to discover that the Pontiff was indeed of the "left foot" persuasion.

That apart, however, I can say that for a time his

visit brought much pleasure to our small, tightly-knit community.

Without exception we were all honoured and "touched to the core" when he agreed, despite a busy schedule of granting private audiences to Mrs Jackie Onassis and coaching Juventus, to make the long and arduous journey from Wopland to the heart of the beautiful and blissful English countryside where in our dear, pure, unsullied village he would open and bestow his blessing on our new cricket pavilion.

In all honesty I am bound to admit that the Pontiff was not our first choice.

Miss Jan Leeming's unavailability caused universal distress and gnashing of teeth, and the indisposition of Miss Louise Botting caused strong men to weep in anguish and despair.

The committee pondered long and hard and in vain until at length old Farmer Emburey spoke out.

"You knows that old bugger we keeps seeing on the telly dressed all in white with a funny hat?" he said.

"Yes," said Prodger the Poacher. "It's Bob Willis."

"No, it ain't, you daft old sod," said Farmer Emburey. "It's thingermejig."

"Who's thingermejig?" said Gooch the blacksmith.

"You knows," said Farmer Emburey. "It's whatchermecallit. Him what is adored by millions and worshipped as the fount of all bleeding knowledge."

"Ah," said PC Jesty. "You mean Michael Parkinson."

"No, I doesn't, you barmy old twat," said Farmer Emburey. "I mean him what brings solace to the sick, look, comfort to the weary, succour to the distraught and strength and eternal hope to the lovelorn."

"Colin Dredge!" said Miss Roebuck from the dog biscuit shop and collapsed instantly into a dead swoon.

As usual she was revived by the application to her rib cage of the massed boot ends of the committee and in next to no time "business was resumed".

After long deliberation the identity of Farmer Emburey's candidate was discovered, and it was agreed that "approaches" would be made to him, if, as we suspected, Edmundo Ros would turn us down again.

This was indeed the case and our secretary, Mrs Botham, wife of the village mail order chiropodist, wrote the following letter:

Dear Pope,
As you've no doubt heard we've built a new pavilion at Witney Scrotum, look, with indoor urinals and working shower attachments.

Well, we wants someone to open it, look.

I myself plumped for Roy Orbison, but owing to the fact that I myself personally was democratically over-ruled we've settled for you, look, and we hopes you'll be able to oblige.

There will be a sit-down tea, a few speeches, a bit of a piss-up and your fee will be five pounds in oncers.

I do hope you'll be able to oblige.

Much to my surprise the response of the Holy Father was swift and decisive.

Yes, he said, he would be delighted to oblige and could we provide a separate WC for the Blessed St John Stevas.

And thus it was that on an early June morning of warblered breezes and swift-winged sunshine the villagers gathered as one on the cricket green and raised their respective, individual hats aloft to welcome the arrival of the Servus Servorum Dei in his Air Eyetie Popecopter.

On alighting the Holy Father immediately fell to his hands and knees and kissed the cricket pitch just short of a length outside the leg stump.

"Silly old sod," said Farmer Emburey. "He's made a bloody wet spot for their leg spinners, look."

But that apart there was not a murmur of complaint as the villagers stood enraptured while the Pope introduced the dazzling array of church dignitaries who had accompanied him.

There was Cardinal Bailey with his familiar hooded eyelids, dropped aitches and ecumenical paunch.

There was Monsignor Tavare proudly holding aloft the ceremonial incense-soaked cricket bat said to have been used by Paul of Tarsus in his celebrated first confrontation with Norman Gifford.

And there, representing the massed ranks of the non-"brown-hatters" were Archbishop Fred Rumsey of the Church of England, Doctor Tony Lewis of the Free and Totally Hypocritical Temperance Church in Wales, the Venerable Munificence Alvin Kallicharran of the Coptic Church in Edgbaston and, leading the General Synod of the MCC, the lugubrious Innersole in his full ceremonial regalia of Aertex baldachin and Bukta khaki buskins.

Passing through the honour guard of a detachment of Don "Sir Oswald" Mosey's junior Blackshirts and accompanied by the music of the Keating New Town Girl Pipers, the Holy Father climbed into the back of the specially constructed Poperoller and commenced his tour of our village.

With deep and moving reverence he inspected some of our most sacred shrines.

Candles were lit before the altar of St Kevin de Keegan, the patron saint of endorsements and home perms.

Prayers were said in the grotto where the saintly Mary Poppins-Parkinson first saw her vision of breakfast television.

And a special cricketers' mass was said on the very spot where the immortal Tony Greig of the Sorrows saw Mr Donald "Deborah" Carr turned into a pillar of salt by Mr Kerry Packer, who at the time was wearing his face inside out.

These solemn duties having been undertaken with dignity and most moving ceremonial, it was time for the festivities to begin.

In honour of our visitors from Italy, Miss Roebuck and her ladies from the social committee had prepared a special Dago luncheon consisting of Heinz spaghetti hoops, Birds Eye aubergine and marmalade frozen pizzas and Quaker macaroni pudding.

The greedy scum wolfed it down with unrestrained glee and, after the whole assembly had quaffed gallons of untreated scrumpy and homemade Marmite Chianti, the Pope opened the pavilion in eighty-seven foreign languages.

"Sounds just like that Freddie Trueman," said Farmer Emburey as the Holy Father concluded the Flemish version of his speech.

Shortly after came the "highlight" of the celebrations – a special cricket match between Witney Scrotum and a Vatican Select XI skippered by the Pontiff himself.

I wish, oh, how I wish that I could find it in my heart of hearts to term it a resounding success.

It is possible, of course, that our visitors were unaware of the niceties of the laws of our beloved "summer game".

Charitably a case could be made out for stating that their scorer, the Blessed St John Stevas, might have been overwhelmed by the attentions of Miss Roebuck from the dog biscuit shop, who took an instant "shine" to him.

Nonetheless I am bound to say that there can be no possible excuse for the "scenes" which ensued when the match was declared a tie by the two umpires, old Squire Brearley, representing our village, and Mother Cliff Richard, representing the RCs.

The match started amicably enough.

We won the toss and elected to bat.

Despite a ferocious spell of new ball bowling by Mary O'Hara and Lady Antonia Frazier, our opening pair Gooch and the younger Graveney from the temperance hamster farm put on an undefeated 39 until Gooch was caught off a "skier" from the Papal Nunciate to Bramall Lane.

The Holy Father himself showed himself to be the possessor of a fiendish leg tweak, although his control of length and line "left something to be desired".

There was a good spell of hostile military medium seam-up from Edna O'Brien, which only ended when she was excommunicated by Mother Cliff Richard for being rude in the region of third man.

However, despite one or two alarums and excursions we concluded our innings for a sedate 197 for 7 declared, and felt well satisfied with our labours.

Tea was taken, during which Prodger the Poacher

entertained the guests with his celebrated mono-
logue, "The One-Legged Stumper of Old Port Said"
and Miss Roebuck from the dog biscuit shop
presented a lantern slide lecture entitled, "An
Illustrated History of the Pin Up Umpire in County
Cricket – Bill Alley to Merv Kitchen".

And then it rained.

It rained and it rained and it rained.

Soon the outfield was flooded and the wicket was
a maelstrom of unrestrained water courses.

What was to be done?

Old Squire Brearley pored long and hard over the
King James Bible but could find not a single
reference to a match having been declared abandoned under such circumstances.

The lugubrious Innersole and his fellow members
of the General Synod of the MCC were "locked" in
deep discussion over the vexed question of the
ordination of women umpires into the first class
game and could not be disturbed to give an opinion.

An extra day's play was impossible – the Pope was
free but Gooch had an appointment with his
dentist.

Finally, after long and careful deliberation and
consultations with all "interested parties", the two
umpires, old Squire Brearley and Mother Cliff
Richard, rose to their feet and declared the match a
tie.

It seemed that honour had been satisfied.

But then of a sudden there burst into the pavilion

long room the wild and gibbering figure of Dr Jones-Jones-Ontong-Wooller.

His eyes were flashing, his lips were slavering, his elbows were quaking. Oh, my God, I thought, he's been on the sacramental Brains Dark again.

Such was the ferocity of his mien and the viciousness of his features that the whole congregation was reduced to instant silence.

He surveyed us for what seemed an eternity – longer by far than an opening sermon by Monsignor Tavare at Tunbridge Wells.

And then he spoke.

"A tie?" he said. "A tie?"

And at first his voice was soft and soothing.

And then it rose to a crescendo.

"A tie?" he screamed.

"Typical of the Papists.

"Oh ye of little wisdom.

"Oh ye of gutless faith.

"Duped it is you have been.

"Have not the valleys of Glamorgan been suborned and poisoned by the invaders from across the Dyke?

"Have you learned no lessons from the tyrannies of the vile Sir Oswald de Wheatley, the heresies of Miandad, the purple platitudes of Hobbs and the infallibility of Selvey?

"Stand up for your faith.

"Keep cricket pure and simple and free from the invaders from overseas who . . ."

The rest of his words were drowned as the congregation screamed out in anger and in approbation.

I confess that in a life spent in "active service" for King and country in some of the foulest hell-holes of modern warfare I have never seen such sickening violence.

Never shall I forget the sight of the Blessed St John Stevas standing on top of the smouldering tea urn, skirts tucked up under his armpits, screaming in blind panic as PC Jesty belaboured Cardinal "Joe" Hume with his Duncan Fearnley truncheon.

Never shall I erase from memory the vision of Lord Longford elbow wrestling with Miss Popplewell from the Overseas Bible and *Wisden's Almanack* Society while pint pots flew in all directions and old Grannie Swanton enfiladed the massed ranks of the College of Cardinals with cricket balls from the fast bowling machine.   .

I could stand it no longer.

Under cover of darkness I crept home.

On reaching my front gate I noticed a light peeking under the front door of the Commodore's summer house.

I went inside.

The Commodore instantly put his finger to his lips.

"Shush," he said. "I have a visitor."

He tip-toed into the inner sanctum where on long, cold winter nights we swapped cigarette cards and compared engine spotter's notes.

"Look," he said.

I peered hard into the gloom and there, sleeping blissfully on the hump-backed couch, was a small silver-haired figure wearing nothing but a long white nightshirt and white cricket cap with no peak.

"Good God," I said. "Do you know who it is?"

"Of course I do," said the Commodore. "It's Bob Berry of Lancashire and Derbyshire."

"No, no, no," I said. "It's the Pope."

The Commodore stared silently at his guest for some moments.

I had the ghastly thought that he was going to tip him out of the couch and turf him out into the cold, limp night by the scruff of the neck.

But then he smiled.

And he took out a large plaid horse blanket and gently laid it over the sleeping figure.

"Well, if there's one thing this visit has taught me, it's the virtue of tolerance and the need to fight intolerance ceaselessly and vigilantly," he said.

And he smiled again, and he said:

"Do you think RCs eat cooked breakfasts like we do?"

NINE

'Looknow" Hobson

Of all the multifarious legions of offensive and verminous people I have encountered during my long and happy association with the "summer game" none can compare in vileness of temper, loathsomeness of manner and ugliness of mien with "Looknow" Hobson.

I first met him as a young boy long long ago, when visiting my beloved uncle, who served as auxilliary suffragan rural deacon and knocker-up in the Lancashire village of Cardus-in-Tyldesleydale, set in the glorious heart of that magnificent northern scenic jewel, the Trough of Bolus.

Uncle Hornby had "taken up" the church some ten years previously, having successfully concluded a productive and distinguished career in dried fruit.

Through a life-long mutual interest in strong drink, loose women, flatulence and cricket he forged a firm friendship with the "then" Archbishop of Lancaster, the Very Reverend Doctor Harold Makepeace-Poidevin.

Strings were pulled in "high places" and in next

to no time my uncle found himself granted the living of Cardus-in-Tyldesleydale on the understanding that he supplied his own bicycle and puncture outfit.

Much to his surprise Uncle Hornby was an outstanding and instant success with his parishioners.

Within a week he had been appointed Hon. President of, among many other institutions, the Ladies' Keep Fit and Hound Trailing Society, the Men's Indoor Knitting Circle and the village WI branch of the Harley Davison Roadburners' Club.

It was, however, in the sphere of cricket that he achieved his greatest triumphs.

His fame as a preacher cascaded down the valley and into the hills and folk from many miles distant tramped across the rugged high fells to hear him preach at the services of All Hallows, Parkin Sunday, the Purification of Garlick and the Conversion of Paynter to Opening Bat.

It was quite natural, therefore, that Uncle Hornby should be drawn "willy nilly" into a deep involvement in the affairs of the village cricket club.

At the time of his arrival its condition was parlous. For three successive seasons it had finished at the bottom of the second division of the Trough of Bolus and Sibbles Valley League and for five years had been knocked out in the first round of the Statham Cup.

No wonder its finances were on such a disastrous footing.

There was so little money available for essential services that visiting teams were presented with gin trap and poacher's blunderbuss and told to trap their own tea.

The communal toenail clipper was rusted up "beyond redemption", there were dippers nesting in the umpires' urinals, and the permanent standing water on the pitch served as the home for wildfowl such as duckworth and pollard, spoonerbill and the rare Philipson's pratincole.

My Uncle Hornby took one look at the situation and said decisively:

"There is one man and one man alone who can save us."

And thus four days later did "Looknow" Hobson take up residence in the village.

He arrived on a blissful morning of early spring.

The Lancashire countryside looked at its best.

Ravens plunged and pirouetted high above the distant fells.

Lambs bleated.

Curlews creamed and crumbled the fresh young breezes, and in the far sea-scented haze the sun glinted like soft pollen on the broad estuary of the River Sibbles.

"Splendid day, eh, Hobson?" said my uncle slapping him warmly on the back. "Wonderful, eh?

Makes a man feel glad to be alive."

"Oh, does it?" said Hobson and he curled his lips, narrowed his eyes and trudged away, stoop-shouldered, to his temporary quarters in the attic of the eccles cake repository.

It was not long before Hobson had impressed himself forcibly and indelibly on every aspect of village life.

What was the secret of the dominance he held, the fear he purveyed, the awe he created in the hearts and minds of the simple and kindly villagers?

Was it the long sad sigh and slough of his drinking boots as he slumped prostrate each night to the floor of "The Monkey and Barber"?

Was it the wet sluck of his india rubber dentures or the constant malignant glare of the blind boil on the end of his nose?

Was it the way small mammals quaked and howled shrilly in the hedgerows as he passed by at dawn, with his bald ferret snarling in his hip pocket and his pet constipated long-eared owl scowling on his shoulder?

That is possible, dear readers.

It is more likely, I feel, that their fear and apprehension was the result of the singular manner in which he was wont to communicate with his fellow human beings and cricket lovers.

"How do, Hobson," the village undertaker, Wharton, would say. "Nice day today, eh?"

And Hobson would reply:

"Don't look like that. It's nowt to do wi' me."

Or the village dentist, the dashing Mr Cranston, would say:

"Whatho, Hobson. Looks as though we're in for a bit of the old Jupiter Pluvius, what?"

And Hobson would reply:

"Don't look like that. It's nowt to do wi' me."

And still remembered vividly by the more elderly villagers was the occasion when the thoroughly nice Mr Greenwood of the steam laundry said:

"Good news, Hobson. My wife's expecting a baby."

And Hobson replied:

"Don't look like that. It's nowt to do wi' me."

But what puzzled and disturbed most the kindly and homely natives of the blessed county of the nonpareil red rose was Hobson's curious obsession with one mode of speech which was to give him his nickname and engrain itself deep into the memories of all who knew him.

Many is the time I have heard my Uncle Hornby say:

"Morning, Hobson. Had any good bowel movements lately?"

And Hobson would reply:

"Not bad. Not as good as Looknow. That was the place for good bowel movements – Looknow."

I remember so well dear timid Miss Greenhough

from the mixed badminton club saying in that blushful, decorous and shy manner that was so distinctively hers:

"Good morning, Mr Hobson. Isn't it a lovely day?"

And Hobson replied:

"Is it buggery. Looknow. That's the place for nice days – Looknow."

And I myself once approached him when very young during the glorious height of a smoke-wreathed, grouse-clacking, berry-bursting Lancashire autumn and said:

"Hullo, Mr Hobson. Do you fancy a game of conkers?"

And he said:

"Piss off, you little twat. If you want to play conkers, go to Looknow. Looknow. That's the place for conkers – Looknow."

That night I pondered long and hard over what he had said.

I consulted reference books and back numbers of the *National Geographic Magazine* in my Uncle Hornby's gruff and gloomy study.

Next day I timorously approached Hobson as he was paring his fingernails with the horse drawn gang mower and said:

"Excuse me, Mr Hobson. Looknow? Isn't that in India? Isn't that the capital of Uttar Pradash? Wasn't it the capital of the ancient Nawabs of Oudh? Isn't its main trade in oilseeds, chemicals and brass articles?''

And he snarled his lips and scowled his eyes and he said:

"Don't look like that. It's nowt to do wi' me."

So why was he tolerated?

The answer is simple.

It lies in one word.

Why did Revnell and West open the innings for the BBC Talking Wireless XI for ten years running at the Bath Festival?

Why did the immortal Collinson and Breen, "Someone's Pinched Me Puddin'", top the bill for so long at Blackpool's Central Pier despite the fierce and relentless competition of Washbrook and Place, "Someone's Pinched Me Wisden's"?

How on earth did that booby with the big ears and the bald patch come to marry the divine, exquisite, radiant, doe-eyed Princess of Wales?

Yes.

In one word it is this – success.

Admittedly "Looknow" Hobson never personally piloted an Andover of the Queen's Flight, or single-handedly captained a moving minesweeper, or discovered the resting place of the *Mary Rose* or played polo for Dewhursts the Butchers or invented Sir Harry Secombe.

But, by God, he achieved success beyond measure in "his own field".

He was the finest groundsman ever to be encountered the length and breadth of the Duchy of Lancaster and was beyond compare as a slow right-arm tweaker and a hurricane left hand slogger.

And thus was he tolerated in Cardus-in-Tyldesleydale.

The transformation he wrought in the affairs of the village and its cricket team was truly remarkable.

First he "set to" on the pavilion.

Night after night the village echoed to the hammering of nails, the sawing of wood and the howling of foul imprecations.

Within a month the rotting, rat-infested hulk had been turned into a veritable cricketing Neuschwanstein with a rosewood and tupelo veneered long room with art deco glasswork and William and Arthur Morris tapestries, with an umpires' rest room decorated in the style of the Basilica of St Peter's in Rome, with a main staircase of finest Florentine marble and a tea room constructed in the manner of purest and highest Bramall Lane baroque.

"Magnificent, Hobson," said my Uncle Hornby. "Truly magnificent."

"Don't look like that," said Hornby. "It's nowt do wi' me."

And he sloped away to his newly-constructed score board made from the front of an open-balconied red Liverpool tram car.

His transformation of the ground was no less remarkable.

He devised an intricate system of dykes, drainage ditches, sluices and windmills and before spring was out had removed the huge area of standing water, thus, incidentally, depriving the rare and beautiful Tattersall's bartailed godwit of its last wintering place in the British Isles.

The square itself he completely re-laid during the course of one single night, although the villagers were much puzzled that this operation took place out of sight behind stout canvas sightscreens, from which ascended dense clouds of curry-scented steam.

As a cricketer his influence on the club was no less profound.

He had no peer as a tweaker of leg breaks and googlies.

On sticky dog or feather bed he could make the ball turn a yard either way, fizz viciously head high off a perfect length, and there was not a batsman the length and breadth of the league who could face him in confidence.

As a smiter of mighty sixes, as a match winner from "impossible situations" he had no equal.

Five years after his arrival in the village the team had risen from the depths of the second division in one season and for the four following seasons accomplished the double of the Statham Cup and the League Championship.

What a professional!

I maintain, however, that his finest talent of all was as a groundsman.

There are practitioners of that noble art, who, not to "put too fine a point on it", can doctor pitches to suit their own bowlers.

In my opinion this is a perfectly valid operation.

After all in every household the man is accustomed as a matter of right to employ all manner of subterfuges in order to dissuade his lady wife's loathsome unmarried spinster sister from Cheltenham from staying in his house, these varying from over-watering her eiderdown and spiking her pyjama case to filling her scent bottles with linseed oil.

Knowing "Looknow" Hobson as I did, I am pretty certain that in that sphere of activities he would have been supreme.

However, of one thing I am absolutely positive.

He excelled at an art no groundsman before or since has ever mastered – the doctoring of pitches during a match.

How he did it no one ever knew.

Certainly in the dead of night he could be seen, a misty, distant, oath-croaking figure, brewing strange potions in a cast iron pot on an open fire at the rear of the pavilion.

There were those who once or twice passed

comment on the long waterproof combinations with funnel attachment at the waist and wooden bung at the bottoms, which he habitually wore beneath his flannels during the course of matches.

All of us, however, would watch in fascination as "Looknow" Hobson during the interval between innings would walk slowly up and down the pitch, tugging at the cord in his waistband and straightening and flexing his legs, thus turning it instantly from a sticky dog to a slow feather bed, or from a fast true-pitcher to a medium-paced uneven shooter.

Our opponents were baffled.

Put in to bat on a spitting turner, they would scramble to 88 and with grins of triumph on their faces say:

"Not bad, was that? Wait while we get you buggers on it."

And then during the interval "Looknow" Hobson would stalk slowly up and down the pitch and of an instant it would be changed to a true and even medium-pacer and we would win by 8 wickets.

Whatever type of wicket was needed for the team at whatever juncture during the match "Looknow" Hobson would provide it.

Some suspicious souls among the opposition maintained that "jiggery pokery" had taken place.

But no one could prove it.

Certainly the members of the village team "kept their thoughts" to themselves.

Once I plucked up courage and said to Hobson after a pitch had been miraculously transformed from a lifeless pudding to a vicious pancaking spitter:

"How do you do it, Hobson?"

And for the first time I saw a grin appear on his face.

However, of an instant it disappeared to be replaced by his habitual scowl and snarl, and he said:

"Don't look like that. It's nowt to do wi' me."

No wonder then that despite his revolting, disgusting and totally anti-social behaviour he was "accepted" into the village.

Well might have he continued in that vein until the time came, as come it must for all lovers of the "summer game", when the length grows shorter, the arm droops lower and all activity ceases in the nether regions of the popping crease, and it is time to clamp firmly shut the padlock on old Father Time's abdominal protector.

Unfortunately for "Looknow" Hobson there occurred an event which was to have profound and disastrous consequences on the whole future conduct of his life – his mother arrived in the village.

She "turned up" one morning in the weekly petrol-powered charabanc from Market Ikin and announced her presence by bellowing at the top of her voice:

"I'm looking for Hobson."

My Uncle Hornby, ever the perfect gentleman, hurried out of the saloon bar of "The Monkey and Barber", where he was conducting rehearsals for the celebrations of Stumper's Sunday, and endeavoured to assist her.

"Perhaps, madame," he said, "you could tell me the nature of your identity."

She looked him up and down.

A snarl came to her lips and a scowl to her eyes.

"I am his mother," she said. "Don't look like that. It's nowt to do wi' me."

With a gentle bow of his head my Uncle Hornby directed her to the simple attic above the eccles cake repository which was the abode of the lady's son.

It was to be "the end" of an era.

For two days nothing was seen of Hobson and his mother, and then came "the bombshell".

Mrs Hobson, a formidable lady with a military moustache, Hapsburg jaw and the bearing of a semi-dismounted Uhlan, presented herself in front of the cricket committee and demanded instantly on behalf of her son:

A 300 per cent increase in his groundsman's salary.

A 250 per cent increase in his professional's salary.

And private quarters in a penthouse suite above the pavilion clock and free supplies of drink and victuals from "The Monkey and Barber".

If these were not provided, she said, the services of her son would be withdrawn forthwith.

For the first time since his arrival in the village "Looknow" Hobson looked discomfited.

He lowered his head and said in a soft voice:

"Looknow. That was the place for withdrawing your services – Looknow."

The committee deliberated long into the night.

Their decision was to be memorable.

"Looknow" Hobson, they said, was still under contract for the rest of the season, and thus would they call his mother's bluff.

The consequences were swift and spectacular.

Pitches ceased to favour our team.

The bald ferret which used to gnaw holes in our visitors' cricket bags and the constipated owl which perched on the sightscreen, flapping its scrawny wing when our opponents were facing the new ball, disappeared.

The pavilion roof began to leak and crumble.

The dippers returned to the umpires' ablutions.

Standing water heralded the resumption of visits from Tattersall's bartailed godwit and the even rarer Grieves's stilt.

And, worse still, "Looknow" Hobson began to disobey orders.

"Bowl him your googly, Hobson," my Uncle Hornby would say.

And Hobson would respond with a long hop off-cutter to leg.

"Push in your top spinner, Hobson," Uncle Hornby would say.

And Hobson would send down a slow full toss.

And from being a slogger of awesome violence and strength, he turned overnight into a blocker of pawky shiftiness.

And all the time his mother with her military moustache and her Hapsburg jaw would sit on the boundary with a smirk of triumph on her face.

Matters came to a head at the end of the season, when, despite Hobson's defections from duty, the village team was in contention for its sixth successive title.

It was a home match against the "arch" rivals, East Hiltonshire.

The visitors batted first and "notched" up a respectable total of 221 on a wicket that was "far from benign".

Uncle Hornby, the skipper, said during the tea interval *sotto voce* to Hobson:

"Right, 'Looknow,' here's your great chance. What about a slow turner?"

Hobson looked at him with a baleful smile and his shoulders hunched up in an attitude of the deepest despair.

"Slow turner?" he said. "Don't look like that. It's nowt to do wi' me."

During the course of the village team's innings the wicket began to jump and spit most savagely.

At 87 for 6 the cause looked lost.

And then Uncle Hornby was joined by the villaged stumper, Parr, himself no mean performer on the church organ, or in the Market Ikin Temperance Silver Band.

Run by run the score crept up to 177.

Twenty runs later and the team was in "with a chance".

Then a foolhardy call by Uncle Hornby and Parr was run out by the length of a tenor saxophone.

The crowd was hushed with anticipation as "Looknow" Hobson came out to bat.

Twenty-three runs to win.

Two overs to go.

Surely with Hobson at the wicket, his shoulders flexed, his biceps rippling, victory was "in the bag".

Uncle Hornby strode down the wicket towards him.

"Right Hobson," he said. "You know what you have to do."

Hobson smiled the most ghastly of grimaces.

"A man cannot serve two masters," he said.

"What?" said my Uncle Hornby. "What's that you say?"

Hobson shook his head slowly.

"Looknow," he said. "That's the place for being buggered up – Looknow."

And so he took the bowling.

The first five balls he blocked.

The crowd bayed in disbelief.

My Uncle Hornby jumped up and down in rage. It was no use.

At the end of the first over Hobson took a single and refused the easy second run.

For the final over he blocked each ball, patting back to the bowler long hop, full toss and grubber.

Defeat.

The victory and the championship went to East Hiltonshire.

For three days the village was in a state of numbed shock.

And then a special meeting of the cricket committee was called.

Hours later in the dead of night there came the sound of marching feet.

Dear Miss Greenwood swears that, peeping out of her dear lace curtains, she saw a special detachment of the J. A. Fallows Fencibles marching through the village.

Certainly every single soul in the village heard beyond doubt and peradventure a volley of rifle shots ring out from behind "The Monkey and Barber".

Next morning the silent villagers lined the streets

and bowed their heads as, loaded on to the back of the horse-drawn carrier's cart, was a large metal trunk.

And on its side was written in large letters:

"To Looknow. Any Side Up."

We never saw Hobson again.

Neither did we see his mother.

After the fateful match against East Hiltonshire she simply disappeared off the face of the earth.

And then many years later there occurred a most singular event.

Uncle Hornby and I were blackberrying in the coarse meadows at the confluence of the rivers Sibbles and Tyldesley, and there in the deepest recesses of a tangled bush we found a skeleton.

It had the vestiges of a military moustache and a distinctive Hapsburg jaw.

And round the neck of the skeleton hung a card.

And on the card was written:

"Don't look like that. It's nowt to do wi' me."

TEN

Miss Roebuck's Diaries – The Journals of a Cricketing Spinster

There are times when I feel that my good friend, the Commodore, is being slightly less than charitable in his attitude towards spinster ladies.

"Bloody things," he says. "They should all be put down at birth."

Whilst I have some sympathy for his attitude, particularly when appertaining to the lady wife's loathsome unmarried spinster sister from Cheltenham with her flat feet, her damp teeth and her felt-tipped pens, I do feel that on certain occasions "allowances" must be made for the breed's innate vileness and comprehensive repulsiveness.

I, for example, am always perfectly ready to take a sympathetic attitude to the oddities of dear Miss Roebuck's behaviour at pollination time.

The dreamy smile as she stands behind the counter of the dog biscuit shop, picking her teeth with the stem of a millet spray and discreetly scratching her buttocks with the blunt end of a cuttlefish bone, is the result of deep, natural forces, which we chaps of the masculine gender, with our distinctive hairy ear holes and ginger plus-fours, are physiologically incapable of understanding.

It is something profoundly atavistic and totally unique to the female gender – yes, like countless thousands of her sex and status, she is in love with Colin Dredge.

Better to leave her to her reveries.

Call back an hour later for your flea collar.

Postpone the purchase of your canine bismuth pills.

When spinsters are locked in the grip of that sensuous, sinuous, overpowering brute animal magnetism of Colin Dredge, all we males of the opposite sex can do is either retire into a dark corner or throw a bucket of cold water over them.

I am prompted to make these reflections after long and careful examination of certain documents which have recently "come into my possession".

The circumstances were thus:

On a bleak winter's afternoon of chill squalls, skudding black clouds and impending pikelets the Commodore and I were returning from our weekly "duty" visit to old Granny Swanton, to whom we had distributed the usual chewing tobacco and brushed denim hot water bottle covers.

We had partaken liberally of the dear old soul's home-made bedsock brandy and were just approaching the blind corner by the Graveneys' temperance hamster farm, when "out of the blue" appeared a figure attired in flapping bright yellow oilskin cape, black Wellington boots and riding a maroon Rudge lady's bicycle with chain guard.

The creature was ringing the bell on its handlebars furiously.

You can imagine our horror when we discovered the reason for this – its view was totally obscured by the sou'wester which had fallen in front of its eyes.

Before we could take evasive action the bicycle struck the Commodore full amidships, caught me a violent and painful blow on the right hip and propelled us both into the ditch at the side of the road, where we were soon joined by the rider of the bicycle in question.

It was none other than Miss Robebuck of the dog biscuit shop.

"Bloody spinster," bellowed the Commodore and commenced to beat her most hideously about the shoulders with the sawn-off niblick he customarily carried for this express purpose.

I managed to placate him and comfort Miss Roebuck.

I placed her on her bicycle and, full of apologies, she wobbled off into the distance.

No sooner had she disappeared and we had "dusted ourselves down" than I discovered lying in the middle of the road a large, leather-bound book, which had obviously fallen out of Miss Roebuck's saddle bag.

On returning home I opened it.

It was her diary.

What a treasure chest of insights into the mind of a lady, who must be typical of the many hundreds of her sex we see at cricket matches the length and breadth of the country.

They sit there placidly knitting or snapping at the passing flies, and they look a picture of contentment.

Only by reading diaries such as those compiled by Miss Roebuck can we discover the torments and the passions which seethe and writhe behind that outward calm.

It is for that reason that I present a selection of extracts from these journals.

I hope Miss Roebuck won't feel I have breached a confidence and come out in a rash on her neck and start swooning and fainting all over the place.

If she does, I shall have no other alternative than to set the Commodore on to her once more with his sawn-off niblick.

So here goes:

Jan 1st:

Only one hundred and fourteen days, seven hours and thirty-three minutes before the start of a new cricket season.

I can hardly wait.

Sent three New Year cards to Colin Dredge.

How my heart flutters at the mention of that name.

Have already started knitting a new cardie for him with leather buttons and military-style elbow patches – my thirty-seventh.

Weather awful.

Seem to have a slight fungal infection on the sole of my right foot.

Jan 15th:

Poor Blake Carrington got shot on the telly the other night.

I could hardly bear to look at the anguish in Nick Toscani's eyes.

Isn't he luscious?

Isn't he the spitting image of Zaheer Abbas?

My God, how I wish I were Louise Botting or even Patti Caldwell if she'd got a nicer accent.

Had a run on Bob Martin's medium strength.

Weather rotten.

Had my third successive dream about Arthur Negus.

Seem to have come out with chilblains again.

Jan 28th:

A new delivery of Purina today.

The van driver was the spitting image of Bob

Taylor – poor old soul.

Sent another bottle of cough mixture to Jimmy Young.

Told him he can share it with the Legal Beagle, if he wants.

Think I might have my hair done à la Princess Di.

Or I might try the Jeff Thomson home perm.

I wonder what Colin Dredge is doing?

I had this dream about him last night.

We were running naked through the water meadows at Cowdrey's Bottom, and he took me in his great manly arms and forced me backwards to the grass and he garlanded my whatsit with cigarette cards, and I felt his sweet-scented breath rilling over my throbbing thingies and then he heaved himself up on his elbows and he . . .

Seem to have come out in a rash on my shins.

Feb 3rd:

When I reach the age of seventy-five like Joan Collins I hope I look like her.

Isn't she the spitting image of Derek Randall – though I don't think her complexion's quite so nice.

Knitted a pair of bedsocks for John Woodcock of *The Times* and sent off same in a registered envelope on which I wrote SWALK.

Sold a budgie bath to Don "Sir Oswald" Mosey.

I'm pretty sure he won't fit into it.

Very rainy today.

Seem to have grown two more white spots on my left thumbnail.

Feb 11th:

Only seventy-two days, six hours and three minutes before the start of another cricket season.

Started knitting a new casual slip-over for Colin Dredge in coloured Fair Isle.

Miss Slocombe from the mobile acupuncturists says she thinks he's "big-headed".

I'll scratch her eyes out one of these days.

Isn't that Henry Kelly on the wireless a pain in the neck?

I can't stand the Irish.

They've such awful teeth.

Seem to have developed a slight infection of the sinus.

Feb 28th:

A glorious day.

Went for a long tramp on my own up Botham's Gut.

Could see for miles and miles and miles.

I felt like taking all my clothes off.

I'd love to roll naked inside Viv Richards's cricket bag provided he promised to take his boots out.

Isn't "Family Fortunes" a dreadful programme on the telly?

They had this family from Sunderland on, and, honestly, one of the sisters-in-law was wearing this home-made dress in shocking pink and you could see all her underskirt and I swear she hadn't shaved her armpits for ages.

It makes me sick.

On my way home Prodger the Poacher exposed himself to me again.

Seem to have been bitten by midges.

March 2nd:

Such excitement in the village.

We're going to be on the telly in "Songs of Praise".

I wonder if they'll send that dishy Geoffrey Wheeler.

I like the name Geoffrey, don't you?

Caught old Granny Swanton shoplifting again.

What she wants with three gerbils and five packets of canary shampoo I'll never know.

Hope I don't get like her when I grow old.

When I grow old I hope I look like Ray Illingworth.

Isn't he the spitting image of Thora Hird?

Seem to have contracted an irritation on the left ear lobe.

March 12th:

Started rehearsals for "Songs of Praise".

I'm on the front row with Miss Slocombe, so I'm bound to be noticed by "you know who".

Had another dream about R. T. Simpson last night.

We put on 227 against Derbyshire without loss, and then I danced naked all night with Arthur Jepson and Harold Butler.

They were very good on the slow foxtrot, but they didn't seem to have the timing for the Latin American dances.

Seem to be in for another bout of my psoriasis.

March 19th:

Disaster.

Calamity.

Woke up on the morning of "Songs of Praise" and discovered my face had erupted in the most awful blotches and pustules.

How could I possibly sit in the front row?

I'd have been mortified if He'd seen me.

Had to sit on the back row next to Prodger the Poacher and old Arlott who kept slurping at his hip flask all through responses.

Still, I did see Geoffrey Wheeler in the flesh.

I wish I were Hannah Gordon.

Walked home in the darkness with Miss Slocombe and Miss Denning from the wireless repair shop.

Prodger the Poacher exposed himself to us again.

April 3rd:

A fantastic day.

What joy and what bliss.

First of all we had the pre-season reception at old Squire Brearley's.

I've never seen so many books in the whole of my life.

He's got the complete set of Biggles.

We had a running buffet with meat paste sandwiches and then, ecstasy on ecstasy, the Squire informed us that next September we were going to play a charity game against . . . wait for it . . . a Colin Dredge Select XI.

Oh my God, I went all damp and quaky.

Will He speak to me?

Will He notice me?

I must get some patterns off Mrs Botham and start planning an outfit.

I think a small two-piece in navy blue and lilac would go down very well, don't you?

Saw Maria Aitken on the telly when I got home.

Isn't she the spitting image of Bob Willis?

Seem to be breaking out in a nervous rash on my elbows.

April 9th:

Rain, rain and more rain.

They made the first cut on the pitch with the gang

mower this afternoon, and the whole village smelled of new-mown grass and clover.

Went to bed with the windows open and had another of my dreams.

I was lying naked in a young spring pasture and Barry Wood was rubbing my ankles and Harry Pilling was stroking my thighs and Roy Tattersall was looking down on me with a quizzical look in his eye.

Had to go downstairs for a drink of water.

Think I'll join the Folio Society.

Have you noticed that ladies who wear black velvet jackets always have their sleeves too long?

Seem to be developing a seg on my left knee.

April 20th:

The first net of the season.

Gooch, the blacksmith, was swanking again.

Honestly I think there's more to life than being able to eat ten cricket balls in five minutes flat and Flymo your hair with one hand, don't you?

Once again I am to be scorer and I felt a certain tingle of satisfaction knowing that already my 3B pencils were all sharpened and at the ready and that I had crotcheted a new seat cover for my Bill Frindall autographed patent scorer's commode.

The first housemartins of the year fluttered overhead as I cycled home on the Rudge and there were bats swooping about the eaves of the golf ball museum.

Isn't village life lovely?

If only there were more eligible men.

Maybe I should kidnap Colin Dredge when he comes here in September and I could give cooked breakfasts and watch him shower and rub his body with . . .

Seemed to have lost my seg, but developed a painful wart on my left little finger.

May 2nd:

Our first "hop" of the season.

I was in charge of the gramophone.

Mostly I played Victor Sylvester and Geraldo but in deference to the "younger bloods" I played a few Brian Poole and the Tremeloes from Granny Swanton's collection of all-time greats.

Had the last waltz with Mrs Botham.

She's very good at reversing, but somehow it "wasn't the same".

On the way home Prodger the Poacher exposed himself to us again.

Miss Slocombe got him with the handle of her umbrella and you should have heard him howl.

Went to sleep wondering what on earth had become of Chick Murray and Maidie.

May 11th:

A complete wash-out.

The first match of the season against Gower St Tolchard's and, blow me, it rained cats and dogs all day and the match was abandoned without a ball being bowled.

Their captain was the spitting image of that Robin Bailey on the telly although his voice was nowhere near as posh.

Made myself a cup of Horlicks before retiring to bed with the windows open.

Couldn't sleep.

Rain lashed down, owls hooted and I had this dream about Fred Rumsey.

He was riding his bicycle completely nude and he was playing the bagpipes.

He wasn't a patch on Andy Stewart.

May 30th:

Train spotters' outing to Didcot with Miss Slocombe and Miss Denning.

Saw King George V "in steam".

There was something very masculine and virile in the sight – pistons pumping, steam snarling, flanks quivering.

Just like the run up of Colin Dredge.

I wonder what it's like to be with him when he's "in steam"?

Oh my God, I just can't wait for September.

Must go to British Home Stores and get a new hat for the great day.

To Miss Denning's for supper.

Marmite sandwiches again!

June 1st:

Isn't it a shame about Stephen from "Dynasty"?

Do you think he's really a homo?

I don't.

I know he got up to things he shouldn't with Ted Dinard and his awful wet mouth, but, I mean, after all look what he did with Claudia and Sammy-Joe and . . .

Do you think there are homos in county cricket?

I suppose there are – worse luck.

I mean, whenever you get a group of men, there's always the odd one out who tries to take advantage, isn't there?

But what a sin to spoil your cricket flannels like that!

Sold another bottle of horse colic remover to Don "Sir Oswald" Mosey.

Seems to be doing him good.

June 30th:

What a depressing month.

Rained cats and dogs non stop and we only

managed to finish one match.

I wish I knew somebody famous.

I once almost stood next to Andy Stovold at the Cheltenham Festival, but that's as close as I've got to being on intimate terms with the rich and the glamorous.

Wouldn't it be marvellous to go on a bicycle tour of Cheshire with Norman Cowans?

Wouldn't it be super to be invited home to afternoon tea by Gladstone Small and go to the flicks with Hartley Alleyne and hold hands in the back row?

Why does it never happen to me?

I think it's my glasses that do it.

Maybe I should wear contact lenses like Geoffrey Boycott.

Maybe I should get a hair transplant, too.

Terrible rumpus in the Baxter Arms last night.

It went on for ages and ages.

I looked outside and saw poor old Arlott lying on his back fast asleep on an empty upturned crate of Bulgarian claret.

He seemed quite happy so I didn't disturb him.

Seem to be perspiring a lot in bed these days.

July 8th:

I wish I didn't look so much like that Mavis in "Coronation Street".

Gosh, I feel so depressed.

Will Mr Right ever come along?

Surely I've got something to offer a gentleman of a cricketing bent?

I'm good at fielding, if my glasses don't fog over.

I can catch one-handed and I'm a fully-qualified graduate of the Bill Frindall Postal College of Score Book Maintenance.

What more could a man ask of a woman?

Had a cold bath and finished my Mars bar before going out for a walk.

Just passing the graveyard when Prodger the Poacher jumped out.

He took one look at me and didn't expose himself.

July 28th:

All my hopes and all my thoughts now centre on that day when You Know Who brings his team to our little village.

What shall I wear for him?

Will lipstick be in order?

He won't think me too forward if I paint my toenails, will he?

Or shall I go "*au naturel*"?

I say it myself, but my complexion is still peaches and cream when I don't get acne, and even Miss Slocombe had been known to compliment me on the shape of my ankles.

Went to bed early and was listening to the wireless when I heard those dreaded words:

"You are listening to BBC Radio Four VHF. If you want to hear 'A Book At Bedtime' you will have to re-tune to Medium Wave and . . ."

Oh God.

I cried myself to sleep.

August 3rd:

Felt ever so much better.

I, Miss Slocombe and Miss Denning from the wireless repair shop went into Keating New Town to choose our new rig-outs for the great day.

We went in Miss Slocombe's Datsun, and it only broke down three times.

Much to my surprise we got fixed up as easily as anything.

I decided on a sensible, classic-cut Vyella tennis shirt in self-coloured cerise with a tartan kilt and those really smart fawn flatties with imitation buckles.

The other two went rather over the top, I thought, but I kept it to myself and just concentrated on enjoying my vegetarian Welsh rarebit in the Engels Tea Rooms.

When we got home we had a lovely "girls' evening" listening to Cliff Richard on the gramophone and pulling our friends to pieces.

I slept sound as a bell and only had to get up once to "obey a call of nature".

I wonder if Colin Dredge ever has to do the same?

Seem to be developing a cold sore on the end of my nose.

August 20th:

Only three hundred and seventy-three hours and twenty-six minutes to go before the match.

All the preparations are made.

Golly, what a great day it will be.

We're having a special pre-match cocktail reception at Squire Brearley's with alcoholic beverages and meat paste sandwiches.

Then there'll be a post-match barbecue, followed by dancing to the Nigel Popplewell Four with fairy lights and balloons coming down from the ceiling.

Witney Scrotum will never have seen anything like it.

Had a good day in the shop, too.

Sold four rubber bones to old Granny Swanton.

They're making a tremendous difference to her gums.

Oh happy, happy me.

Seem to be coming out in a slight attack of knicker rash.

August 29th:

Final meeting of the social committee.

Not a hitch in sight.

Never felt so deliriously rapturously happy in the whole of my life – except perhaps when I was chosen second reserve for the lacrosse first team at school.

Feel deep in my bones that Mr Right is just over the horizon.

Surely I will not be alone for much longer?

Surely the gates to paradise are yawning open and I can step inside to a life of darning socks, letting down turn-ups and doing rude things in bed?

Had another dream about Ken Barlow.

Isn't he a drip?

September 3rd:

Only one day to go.

I could hardly do a thing right I was so excited.

I made a mess of my scrambled eggs.

I burned the toast.

I got the change wrong three times in succession.

I forgot to exercise the goldfish.

But then came the time to shut up shop and relax.

I took a light evening meal of high-baked water biscuits and Kraft cheese slices.

I took a long slow bath with Radox.

I set out my new rig-out on tissue paper on the sofa.

And then quite naked I opened the bedroom window and looked out over the village.

The sky was bright and twinkling with a myriad of stars.

Cattle were lowing contentedly.

Barn owls floated on soft wings above the water meadows at Cowdrey's Bottom.

And there gleaming white in the shadows cast by the spire of our dear parish church was the sinuous, sensuous shape of the marquee, standing proud and erect on the cricket ground.

Will I dance with Him there?

Will He take me in his strong manly arms and twirl me to the rhythms of tango and foxtrot?

Will He take me by the hand and lead me to the long-leg boundary and whisper in my soft pink ears and plight His troth?

Went to bed, spirits soaring and rollers purring.

Never felt fitter in the whole of my life.

September 4th:

Disaster.

Total, utter complete calamity.

Woke up on the day of the match and discovered I was covered from head to foot in spots.

Chicken pox!

Confined to quarters.

O death, where is thy sting?

O grave, thy victory?

December 31st:

Only one hundred and twenty days since the day of the match.

Am I down-hearted?

No.

He took 7 wickets for 34 runs.

He caught 8 catches.

He scored 66 in 17 minutes.

And He never once danced with Miss Slocombe or Miss Denning.

Wrote and sent fifteen New Year cards to Him and started knitting a new hand-knit one-piece bed jacket for Him in full county colours.

Oh happy happy me.

He is still mine.

I can still dream.

I can still . . .

Seem to be developing writer's cramp.

ELEVEN

The Brigadier in Season

It is winter in Witney Scrotum.

Fast flows the River Buse through the frost-cropped water meadows at Cowdrey's Bottom.

Wild skeins of snow cloud trail their cold and flimsy skirts across the massive buttress of Botham's Gut.

Harvest mice sleep safe abed in the deep, black-berried pubic tangles around the ancient artesian Popplewells at Dredge's Elbow.

Old Granny Swanton is well lagged against the bitter chills, a night light burns constantly in the seat of her thermal drawers, and every evening before retiring to bed the dear old soul takes without a word of complaint her prescribed three table-spoonfuls of Esso antifreeze mixture.

Yes, all is well with the world.

As our noble and beloved national bard, E. R. "Elizabeth Regina" Dexter, so memorably put it:

"If winter comes, can spring be far behind?"

It is such profundity and beauty of vision that comforts and warms me as I sit in my study idly blacking in the myriad, menacing teeth on the face of my autographed Biedermayer portrait of Clare Francis, the world's first single-handed authoress and, more creditable by far, mother of that gentle and self-effacing Glamorgan batsman, Arthur.

I am in "my own" country.

The Legal Beagle is in full flood with Jimmy Young on the talking wireless.

Our adored Clay Jones still rills and ripples his Celtic cadences on "Gardeners' Question Time".

Despite all the vicissitudes and calamities and disasters and overpowering dangers of this modern world Friday Night is still Music Night.

England!

How better can we express our emotions than through the words of the immortal bard of Langridge-on-Sea, E. R. "Elizabeth Regina" Dexter:

"England bound in with the triumphant sea.
Whose rocky shore beats back the envious waves."

By God, yes, this dear country of ours is indeed under siege.

Wave after wave of Arabs and Gyppos, Micks and Wogs, hairy-navelled Australians, sex-crazed Maltese brothel-keepers, cleaver-toting Chink restaurateurs and adolescent Frog language students with protruding rucksacks and verminous manners throw themselves on our shores trying to establish a bridgehead of odiousness and vileness deep into the heart of this blessed land of ours.

I am not a prejudiced man, but I have to say, dear readers, that we are under dire threat.

The greatest danger to the civilized world as we know it in England is not the nuclear bomb.

It is not even the records of Mary O'Hara.

It is, quite simply, foreigners.

I am prompted into these thoughts after my recent tour with the MCC Jubilee Missionary Expedition to Dagoland, to which I had the honour of acting as baggage master and deputy personal commode wallah to Archbishop Fred Rumsey.

It was an experience I shall "never forget".

We travelled by moving ocean liner, the SS *Canberra*, formerly the SS *Duleepsinjhi* of blessed memory.

The vessel, despite a complete re-fit, still bore the scars of its long and arduous service as personal private yacht to the Ink Monitor at Number Ten, Lady Falklander.

In the former principal torture chamber, now crudely converted into the first class dining room, were still to be seen quite clearly the marks of Lord Carrington's toenails gouged deep into the lino when the great lady herself personally pulled out his teeth with bulldog clips.

And lash marks from the cat o'nine tails used in

the ritual public flogging of the Blessed St John Stevas still marred the laminated, vomit-proof walls of the Ladies' Over Sixties' Bingo Hall.

However, of these blemishes we were blissfully unaware as we set sail from Southampton, serenaded on our way from the quayside by the massed bands of the Church Lads' Brigade, the Jenni Murray School of Dancing and 13th/24th Ingleby-MacKenzie Temperance Lancers.

We were indeed a truly ecumenical and distinguished party.

Among our numbers was the Bramall Lane Emeritus Professor of Christian Ethics and Dropped Aitches, Doctor Frederick S. Trueman, the Supreme Patriarch of the Ball by Ball Orthodox Commentary Team of Trent Bridge, Cardinal Trevor Bailey and his mother, Pearl, Monsignor Tavare, warden of the Catholic Home for Distressed Kosher Umpires and the leader of the Sunday Day League One Day Revivalist Church in Wales, the Rev. Wilfred Ontong-Wooller.

We bore gifts of edible cricket balls, Tizer-flavoured linseed oil and clockwork effigies of Sir Geoffrey Boycott.

However, these favourable omens were swiftly overshadowed by a doom-laden encounter during our first night "at sea".

The circumstances were thus:

The Rev. Ontong-Wooller and I were sitting at the

dinner table idly dunking our menus in the cream of lascar soup, when some florid-faced, bewhiskered brute in white bum-starver jacket and wrinkled maroon socks seated himself at our table without invitation, helped himself to a large draught of our personal home-brewed corn plaster wine and announced in a loud, overbearing voice:

"Good evening, I am the captain."

You can imagine my feelings of horror, revulsion and total affront.

I turned instantly to the wretch and, cracking it over the knuckles with the prongs of my cake fork, said firmly:

"Sir, when I travel by mobile train from my home in Witney Scrotum to the hellhole of London, I do not expect to have to share my table in the restaurant car with the ticket collector or the engine driver's mate.

"They have the courtesy to bring sandwiches and billycan, which they consume privately in the luggage van.

"And so should you – scum."

At this the brute snarled most vilely, flashed its plastic Woolworth monocle and was only persuaded to leave the table when the Rev. Ontong-Wooller executed a swift, savage bite in the seat of its shiny hindquarters with the sharp end of his Cordle and Nash patent cast iron dentures.

Their followed two days of indescribable misery

and deprivation, during which we were subject to interminable, compulsory lifeboat drill under the supervision of nancy boy waiters and false-eyelashed barmen, who instructed us in the intricacies of flower arranging in an open boat and effecting home perms on our hair, should we be marooned on a desert island with the unctuous Roy Plomley.

The rest of the crew treated us with scarcely-concealed contempt, which prompted the saintly Doctor Frederick S. Trueman to comment in his typical sacerdotal tones at morning service:

"It's all reet for them buggers.

"There's two of us passengers for every one of them.

"No wonder they're leading the life of bloody Riley."

No wonder indeed.

I know for a fact that I was not the only one who felt the strain of "doing our bit" to ensure that the crew's luxury cruise was not too seriously incommoded by the irritation of ministering to the needs of the passengers.

It was with great relief, therefore, that we made our first landfall in Dagoland at Vigo in Spain.

I have to report that the natives there were the typical pock-marked, shifty-eyed, untrustworthy scum endemic to foreign climes, thus making them in retrospect infinitely more attractive than our cabin stewards and our fellow passengers in steerage with their flat caps, smoker's coughs and slack-jawed gormless wives with loud voices and laughs like demented klaxons.

Am I an old cynic, dear readers, when I say that the reception we received from the natives in Dagoland was entirely predictable?

They showed not the slightest interest in the fielding practice session organized by Cardinal Bailey on the quayside.

Indeed most of them seemed intent only on attempting to pinch the respective bottoms of Monsignor Tavare and Mr H. D. "Dicky" Bird, who was vainly trying to teach the rudiments of the LBW laws to a rascally-looking onion-seller with balding, black-dyed hair and hollow cheeks, who bore a marked resemblance, I thought, to Mr Enoch "Sandy" Powell.

Worse was to follow during our subsequent stops at various of the two Iberian nations' disgusting outposts in the Atlantic ocean, all of which, with their rain-sodden weather and stench of rotting crisps, reminded me forcibly of high summer in Melbourne.

We were subjected to abuse, derision and at times downright hostility.

Never shall I forget our sojourn at Las Palmas when Sir Donald "Pearl" Carr's lantern slide lecture to the local Chamber of Commerce, "The Golden

Age of Derbyshire Cricket – George Dawkes to Fred Swarbrook", was most rudely interrupted by a howling, baying mob of unshaven, red-eyed, slimy-toothed brigands, reeking of strong drink and stale body odours and looking for all the world like senior members of the Save Boycott for the Nation Campaign.

Like them, too, they showed not the slightest knowledge of the finer points of cricket and seemed interested only in ripping Sir Donald's Hathersage tweed plus-fours from his person in search of contraband cigarette cards.

What could have been a "nasty situation" was saved when Doctor Frederick S. Trueman stood up in front of the mob and most bravely launched himself into one of his celebrated after-dinner speeches.

By God, it worked, too.

In an instant the rabble was reduced to a state of mass torpor and terminal boredom, and we were able to make our escape.

We fared little better in Madeira.

The native Dagos gazed at our collection of historical cricket impedimenta spread out on the quayside with total incomprehension, although when by means of somewhat explicit sign language the Rev. Ontong-Wooller explained to them the purpose of Mr Ian Botham's abdominal protector they hissed through their teeth with astonishment and several younger members of the female gender fainted on the spot.

It was to be our last port of call and as the island with its maniacal tobogganers, its gaudy and vulgar artificial orchids and its catarrh-croaking clouds sank below the horizon, I confess I felt a sense of overwhelming relief.

We were on our way home to Blighty.

The porpoises leaping and coiling in our wake felt instinctively the intensity of our emotions as we lined the rails dressed "overall".

"Yes, yes," they seemed to say as they leapt out of the azure blue ocean. "We know you're going home to Sue Lawley on the moving television, to Louise Botting on the talking wireless, to the sublime Enid J. Wilson on the *Manchester Guardian*."

"Yes, yes, yes," I shouted to them, wildly waving my straw boater. "And even better – Richie Benaud will still be in Australia."

Later that evening, after an excellent dinner of Goanese sweetbreads in porthole sauce, I repaired to the bar at the front end of the ship, where I got into conversation with a snuff-stained Englishman of mature years who informed me that he was a former professor of Cairo University, where he had been head of the Faculty of Arab Shoplifting.

The poor devil had been dismissed with ignominy three years previously, when the authorities had discovered him trying to pay for a cashmere pullover at the local Marks and Spencer.

He slucked at his pipe thoughtfully and said with feeling:

"Foreigners! Absolute, disgusting, nauseating trash, every man jack of them."

I agreed with him then.

I agree with him now, as I stare out of my study window and watch the roost-bound gulls flap lazily from the sea and hear the whirr of the shrub-snug wren and smell the languid scents of winter-flowering jasmine.

And I think of those inspiring lines written by that towering poetic genius, E. R. "Elizabeth Regina" Dexter, to the Dark Lady of the Sonnets, Dame Joel Garner:

> "This England never did, nor never shall
> Lie at the proud foot of conqueror."

By God, how right he is.

But, dear readers, we shall never beat the greasy foreigner by conflict.

We shall not vanquish him by force of arms or by moral rectitude.

No.

We shall keep him for ever from our shores by baffling the living daylights out of him.

How?

Bring back the half crown piece and the three-penny bit.

Stand up and fight for the rod, perch and pole.

Away with Datsun and Toyota.

Welcome back Lanchester and Lea-Francis.

Restore Droitwich, Sottens and Daventry to the dials of our talking wireless sets.

Away with Yamaha and Honda motorbikes.

Welcome back Norton and AJS.

But, above all these, I make a plea in the clearest, purest clarion tones – change the calendar.

Look at it, dear readers.

It is totally, shamelessly foreign.

After whom are the days of the week named?

Foreigners – a load of bloody Swedes.

After whom are the months named?

Foreigners – and oily Wops at that.

Let us have a cricketers' calendar.

Let the names of the week be re-named.

Let us start the week with Sohoniday and progress through F. G. Mannday, Dewesday, Wellandsday, Carrsday, C. B. Fryday to Tattersallday.

Let us change the seasons, too.

Do we really need spring, summer, autumn and winter?

No.

All we need are two seasons – the non-cricketing and the cricketing.

Thus would the season from April to September be designated Absolutely Spiffing.

Thus would the season from October to March be

known as Absolutely Frightful.

How the vile foreigners would be confounded.

Only in Britain would Christmas Day fall on Tattersallday the 87th of Absolutely Frightful.

And only in these sceptered isles would the fourth day of the Lords Test be played on F. G. Mannday, the 117th of Absolutely Spiffing.

Admit it, dear readers, it would transform our lives.

Once more this nation of ours would be proud, defiant and, above all, absolutely unique.

Even so, I'll wager I'd still forget that the lady wife's birthday falls next year on Wellandsday, the 17th of Absolutely Frightful.

How sad that supreme and peerless though we are in England, we still share one common institution with the ghastly foreigner.

I refer, of course, to lady wives.